Note to students

The Course
- This book is designed to cover all of the content statements of the Intermediate 2 Chemistry syllabus.

- Information relating to the Prescribed Practical Activities (PPAs) is included at the end of the book.

Your Revision
- Your revision is most likely to be effective if you stop at the end of each page and try to write out the main points.

- You can indicate your knowledge of each statement with a √ in the ❑ at the left hand side.

- Space has been left at the right hand side so that you can make additional notes.

- You can also mark statements with a highlighter pen.

- You are more likely to benefit from your revision if you work at a steady rate and follow a study plan.

- A time-table to help you plan your revision can be found on the next page.

- A lot of calculations in the Intermediate 2 course involve simple proportion.
There are a number of ways of laying out these calculations.
Check with your mathematics teacher if you are unsure about the layout used in this book.

Revision Notes
for
Intermediate 2
Chemistry

D A Buchanan

**(Moray House Institute,
Edinburgh University)**

J R Melrose

**(Lenzie Academy,
Lenzie, Glasgow)**

Published by
Chemcord
Inch Keith
East Kilbride
Glasgow

ISBN   1 870570 69 3

© Buchanan and Melrose, 2000

Printed by Bell and Bain, Glasgow

Study planner

	Revision √			
	1	2	3	4

UNIT 1   Building Blocks

1. Substances
2. Reaction Rates
3. The Structure of the Atom
4. Bonding, Structure and Properties
5. Chemical Symbolism
6. The Mole

UNIT 2   Carbon Compounds

1. Fuels
2. Nomenclature and Structural Formulae
3. Reactions of Carbon Compounds
4. Plastics and Synthetic Fibres
5. Natural Products

UNIT 3   Acids, Bases and Metals

1. Acids and Bases
2. Salt Preparation
3. Metals

PPAs

Unit 1

Building Blocks

1. SUBSTANCES

Elements

❑ everything in the world is made from **elements**

❑ elements cannot be broken down into simpler substances

❑ there are just over one hundred different elements in total

❑ each element has a name and a symbol

❑ for some elements, the symbol is just the first letter of its name; this is always a capital letter,

    e.g. C (carbon), H (hydrogen), S (sulphur)

❑ for some elements, the symbol is from two letters of the name; with two letter symbols only the first letter is a capital,

    e.g. Ca (calcium), He (helium), Si (silicon)

❑ for some elements, the symbol is from the Latin name,

    e.g. Na (sodium from natrium), Ag (silver from argentum)

❑ elements can be solid, liquid or gas; bromine and mercury are the two liquids at room temperature

❑ chemists have classified elements by arranging them in the **Periodic Table**

Group 1 2   3 4 5 6 7 0

H																	He
Li	Be											B	C	N	O	F	Ne
Na	Mg			transition metals								Al	Si	P	S	Cl	Ar
K	Ca	Sc	Ti	V	Cr	Mn	Fe	Co	Ni	Cu	Zn	Ga	Ge	As	Se	Br	Kr
Rb	Sr	Y	Zr	Nb	Mo	Tc	Ru	Rh	Pd	Ag	Cd	In	Sn	Sb	Te	I	Xe
Cs	Ba	La	Hf	Ta	W	Re	Os	Ir	Pt	Au	Hg	Tl	Pb	Bi	Po	At	Rn
Fr	Ra	Ac															

Ce	Pr	Nd	Pm	Sm	Eu	Gd	Tb	Dy	Ho	Er	Tm	Yb	Lu
Th	Pa	U	Np	Pu	Am	Cm	Bk	Cf	Es	Fm	Md	No	Lr

Group 1
alkali metals

Group 7
halogens

Group 0
noble gases

❑ elements can be metals or non-metals; the metals are on the left-hand side of the Periodic Table

❑ elements can be naturally occurring or made by scientists; the elements made by scientists come after uranium at the bottom of the Periodic Table

- ❏ a row of elements in the Periodic Table is called a **period**

- ❏ a column of elements in the Periodic Table is called a **group**

- ❏ elements in the one group show similar chemical properties

- ❏ the **noble gases** is a group of very unreactive elements

- ❏ the **alkali metals** is a group of very reactive metals; as a result these metals are stored under oil

- ❏ the **halogens** is a group of very reactive non-metals

- ❏ the **transition metals** are between Group 2 and Group 3

Compounds

- ❏ compounds are formed when elements react together,

  e.g. sodium reacts with chlorine to form sodium chloride (salt), hydrogen reacts with oxygen to form hydrogen oxide (water)

- ❏ since the elements in a compound are chemically joined, energy is required to break up a compound,

  *e.g. heat energy to break up silver oxide
  electrical energy to beak up copper chloride (in solution)*

- ❏ **-IDE** compounds usually contain only the two named elements,

  e.g. sodium sulphide contains only sodium and sulphur

- ❏ metal hydroxides are exceptions; these compounds contain a metal as well as hydrogen and oxygen

- ❏ **-ITE** and **-ATE** compounds contain oxygen as well as the two named elements,

  e.g. both sodium sulphite and sodium sulphate contain sodium, sulphur and oxygen

Chemical reactions

- ❏ chemical reactions always produce new substances

- ❏ chemical reactions can identified by changes in appearance,

  e.g. colour change, solid formed, gas given off

- ❏ chemical reactions which do not involve a change in appearance can be detected by energy changes,

  e.g. a change in temperature

- chemical reactions are taking place all around us in everyday life,

  e.g. burning petrol, digesting food, striking a match, grass growing, iron rusting, epoxy glue setting

Exothermic and endothermic reactions

- an **exothermic** reaction releases energy, usually in the form of heat, to the surroundings

- the surroundings include the container in which the reaction takes place, the air round about and the reaction mixture itself

- if heat energy is released there will be a temperature rise in the surroundings since the latter absorbs the energy liberated by the reaction,

  e.g. the reaction between methane (CH_4) and oxygen (O_2) (burning of methane)

- a reaction in which energy is absorbed from the surroundings is called an **endothermic** reaction,

  e.g. the reaction between barium hydroxide pentahydrate ($Ba(OH)_2.5H_2O$) and ammonium thiocyanate (NH_4CNS)

- if heat energy is absorbed there will be a temperature fall in the surroundings

Mixtures

- mixtures are formed when substances come together without reacting,

  e.g. air is a mixture of gases, mainly nitrogen and oxygen

- the test for oxygen is that it relights a glowing splint

- there is not enough oxygen in the air for the test to be positive

- heat or electrical energy is not required to separate the elements in a mixture,

  e.g. iron can be separated from a mixture of iron and sulphur using a magnet, but not from iron sulphide, the compound

Dissolving

❑ a **soluble** substance dissolves in a liquid

❑ an **insoluble** substance does not dissolve in a liquid

❑ the **solvent** is the liquid in which the substance dissolves

❑ the **solute** is the substance which dissolves in a liquid

❑ a solute can be a solid, a liquid or a gas,
   e.g. sugar (solid), alcohol (liquid), sulphur dioxide (gas)

❑ a **solution** is formed when a solute dissolves in a solvent

❑ in an **aqueous** solution water is the solvent,
   e.g. in an aqueous sugar solution, sugar is the solute and
   water is the solvent

❑ a **saturated** solution is one in which no more substance
   can be dissolved

❑ a **dilute** solution has a lower concentration of dissolved
   substance than a **concentrated** solution

dilute
solution   **concentrated**
solution

❑ a solution is diluted by adding more solvent

State symbols

❑ suffixes can be used after the name or formula to show
   the chemical state of the substances

Suffix	Meaning
(s)	solid
(l)	liquid
(g)	gas
(aq)	dissolved in water

2. REACTION RATES

Rates of reaction

❏ the rate of reaction may be expressed in terms of the changes in concentration(s) of reactant(s) or product(s) in unit time

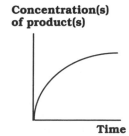

Concentration(s) of reactant(s)

Time

Concentration(s) of product(s)

Time

❏ the reaction rate is most rapid at the start of a reaction and decreases as the reaction proceeds

❏ when a change in concentration is measured in a given time expressed in seconds, the abbreviated unit of rate is mol l^{-1} s^{-1} (moles per litre per second)

❏ average rate of reaction = $\dfrac{\text{change in concentration(s) of reactant(s) or product(s)}}{\text{time taken for the change}}$

Example

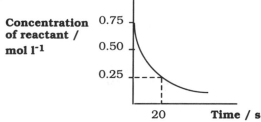

Concentration of reactant / mol l^{-1}

0.75

0.50

0.25

20   **Time / s**

The average rate of reaction over the first 20 s is $\dfrac{0.75 - 0.25}{20}$ = $\dfrac{0.5}{20}$ = **0.025 mol l^{-1} s^{-1}**

❏ since it is not always practicable to measure changes in concentration, changes in mass, in grams, and volume, in cubic centimetres, can also be used to measure rates of reactions; when these changes are measured in a given time expressed in seconds, the abbreviated units are g s^{-1} and cm^3 s^{-1} respectively

Example

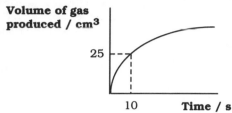

Volume of gas produced / cm³

25

10   **Time / s**

The average rate of reaction over the first 10 s

is $\dfrac{25 - 0}{10}$ = **2.5 cm³ s⁻¹**

❑ the rate of reaction is inversely proportional to time taken, i.e. the rate is proportional to "1/time taken"; this means that, for a fixed change in concentration, the shorter the time taken, the faster the rate of reaction

Successful collisions

❑ for a chemical reaction to occur, reactant particles must collide; this is the basis for the **collision theory**

❑ not all collisions are successful,

> *e.g. nitrogen and oxygen molecules are constantly colliding in the air without a reaction taking place*

❑ this is because energy is required to break all bonds in the reactant molecules before new bonds can be formed,

> *e.g. the reaction of hydrogen with oxygen*

H—H   H–H   O=O   →   O / H H   H–O / H

energy needed to break bonds   **energy released in making new bonds**

Factors which affect reaction rate

(a) Concentration

❑ as the concentration of a reactant increases the rate of collisions increases

**low concentration
of reactants**   **high concentration
of reactants**

❑ this leads to an increase in the rate of successful collisions and hence reaction rate

(b) Particle size

❑ as the particle size decreases the surface area increases

solid particle   **cut into two
pieces**   **new surfaces
exposed**

❑ collisions can occur on the new surfaces;
this leads to an increase in the rate of successful collisions and hence reaction rate

(c) Temperature

❑ the rate of reaction increases as the temperature of the reactants increases

❑ the effect of temperature on reaction rate cannot just be explained on the basis of an increase in the rate of collisions with a rise in temperature

Everyday examples

❑ there is a risk of explosions in flour mills and coal mines since the dust particles are very small (large surface area)

❑ bacterial action on food in a freezer is slower than in a fridge and hence it can be kept longer

❑ an oxyacetylene flame burns at a very high temperature due to the concentration of oxygen

See
UNIT 1 PPA 1

See
UNIT 1 PPA 2

Catalysts

- a **catalyst** speeds up a chemical reaction

- a catalyst takes part in the reaction but is **not** used up by the reaction

- a **heterogeneous catalyst** is one in which the reactants are in a different physical state from the catalyst

- reactions of gases often involve the use of a solid catalyst,

  e.g. iron in the reaction of nitrogen with hydrogen, platinum in the reaction of ammonia with oxygen, vanadium pentoxide in the reaction of sulphur dioxide with oxygen

- reactant particles are **adsorbed** on to sites at the surface of the catalyst

adsorbed particle   **weakened bond**

                                    bond

sites at catalyst surface

- the bonds in the reactant particles are weakened and the particles are in favourable positions

- a collision is likely to be more successful than it would have been without a catalyst

- a reaction takes place and the product particles leave the catalyst surface

- **catalyst poisoning** can occur if impurities are adsorbed on to the surface of the catalyst taking up sites which could otherwise have been occupied by reactant particles

- industrial catalysts have to be **renewed** due to poisoning of the catalysts by impurities in the reactant; when the catalyst is renewed the 'spent' catalyst is removed and replaced by fresh catalyst

- some industrial catalysts which have been poisoned can be **regenerated**; this involves 'cleaning' the catalyst by removing impurity from the active sites, usually by heating with a gas which reacts with the impurity,

  e.g. in catalytic cracking, air is used to burn off carbon from the catalyst

❑ a **homogeneous catalyst** is one in which the reactants are in the same physical state as the catalyst,

    e.g. cobalt ions in the reaction between potassium sodium tartrate and hydrogen peroxide

❑ a homogeneous catalyst takes part in the reaction and is then reformed at the end of the reaction

Uses of catalysts

❑ in many industrial processes catalysts are used to increase reaction rate,

    e.g. an iron catalyst is used in the Haber Process for the manufacture of ammonia, a metal catalyst is used to hydrogenate oils in the manufacture of margarine

❑ catalytic converters are fitted to the exhaust systems of cars to catalyse the conversion of poisonous carbon monoxide and oxides of nitrogen in the exhaust gases to carbon dioxide and nitrogen; these gases are respectively produced by the incomplete combustion of the hydrocarbons in the petrol and the sparking of air

❑ cars with catalytic converters only use 'lead-free' petrol since lead poisons the platinum metal which is used as the catalyst

Enzymes

❑ **enzymes** catalyse the chemical reactions which take place in living cells of plants and animals,

    e.g. amylase in the breakdown of starch during digestion

❑ enzymes are highly specific in the reactions they catalyse, i.e. a particular enzyme will only catalyse a specific reaction or type of reaction

❑ enzymes are active during digestion,

    e.g. amylase, in saliva, helps to convert starch into maltose, the maltose is converted to glucose in the small intestine with the aid of maltase

❑ enzymes are also important in industrial processes,

    e.g. zymase in yeast in the fermentation of sugars to alcohol

3. THE STRUCTURE OF THE ATOM

Sub-atomic particles

❏ every element is made up of very small particles called **atoms**

❏ each element contains only one kind of atom (but see isotopes)

❏ atoms of different elements vary in size and mass

❏ the small core at the centre of the atom is called the **nucleus**

❏ the nucleus contains **protons** and **neutrons** (but note an isotope of hydrogen which has no neutrons)

❏ **electrons** move through space outside the nucleus

❏ the unit used to measure the mass of the sub-atomic particles is the atomic mass unit (amu)

❏ the charge, mass and position in the atom of the sub-atomic particles are as shown

	Charge	Mass	Position in the atom
PROTON	+ve 1	1 amu	nucleus
ELECTRON	-ve 1	neglible	energy level (shell)
NEUTRON	zero	1 amu	nucleus

❏ an atom is neutral because the negative charge of the electrons is equal to the positive charge of the nucleus, i.e. the number of protons is equal to the number of electrons (but see ions)

Electron arrangements

❏ electrons are arranged in **energy levels (shells)**

❏ the first energy level can hold up to 2 electrons; the second energy level can hold up to 8 electrons; the third energy level can hold up to 8 electrons

❏ the electron arrangements of atoms of elements are given on page 1 of the Data Booklet

Important numbers

❑ atoms of different elements have a different number in the Periodic Table called the **atomic number**

KEY

Atomic number
Symbol
Electron arrangement
Name

Group 1	Group 2	Group 3	Group 4	Group 5	Group 6	Group 7	Group 0
1 **H** 1 Hydrogen							2 **He** 2 Hellium
3 **Li** 2,1 Lithium	4 **Be** 2,2 Beryllium	5 **B** 2,3 Boron	6 **C** 2,4 Carbon	7 **N** 2,5 Nitrogen	8 **O** 2,6 Oxygen	9 **F** 2,7 Fluorine	10 **Ne** 2,8 Neon
11 **Na** 2,8,1 Sodium	12 **Mg** 2,8,2 Magnesiu	13 **Al** 2,8,3 Aluminium	14 **Si** 2,8,4 Silicon	15 **P** 2,8,5 Phosphorus	16 **S** 2,8,6 Sulphur	17 **Cl** 2,8,7 Chlorine	18 **Ar** 2,8,8 Argon
19 **K** 2,8,8,1 Potassium	20 **Ca** 2,8,8,2 Calcium						

❑ elements are arranged in order of increasing atomic number with elements having similar chemical properties placed in the same group

❑ the number of protons in the nucleus is equal to the atomic number

❑ the atomic number also gives the number of electrons in an atom (but not an ion)

❑ elements in the same group have similar chemical properties because the atoms have the same number of outer electrons

❑ the **mass number** is the total number of protons plus neutrons in the nucleus

❑ the atomic number and mass number allow the number of protons, neutrons and electrons in an atom to be determined

Mass number - not in Periodic Table, has to be given

Atomic number - see Periodic Table

Number of protons - equal to atomic number

Number of neutrons - mass number minus number of protons

Number of electrons - equal to number of protons

Example

Calculate the number of protons, neutrons and electrons in an atom of lithium with a mass number of 7.

3 protons (atomic number)

4 neutrons (mass number minus number of protons)

3 electrons (equal to number of protons)

❏ the atomic number and mass number are often written with the chemical symbols as shown

$$\text{mass number} \longrightarrow {}_y^z\text{O} \longleftarrow$$

mass number ──── z

atomic number ──── y   O

Example

Calculate the number of protons, neutrons and electrons in the atom:

$$^{35}_{17}\text{Cl}$$

17 protons (atomic number)

20 neutrons (mass number minus number of protons)

17 electrons (equal to number of protons)

Isotopes

❏ **isotopes** are atoms of the one element with different mass numbers

❏ isotopes have the same atomic number, i.e. number of protons, but different mass numbers, i.e. numbers of neutrons

❏ the **relative atomic mass** is the average mass of an atom of an element allowing for the different isotopes present and their percentage proportions

❏ since it is an average, the relative atomic mass is usually **not** a whole number,
e.g. the relative atomic mass of chlorine is 35.5

❏ the relative atomic masses of some elements are given on page 4 of the Data Booklet; these values are rounded to the nearest 0.5

4. BONDING, STRUCTURE AND PROPERTIES

Stable electron arrangements

❑ the noble gases are **unreactive** elements

❑ atoms of these elements have **filled outer energy levels**; these electron arrangements are stable

❑ helium has 2 electrons in the outer energy level

❑ neon, argon, krypton and xenon have 8 electrons in the outer energy levels

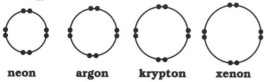

neon	**argon**	**krypton**	**xenon**

Bonding

❑ atoms can be held together by **bonds**

❑ atoms which are bonded together tend to have the same electron arrangements as atoms of the nearest noble gases

❑ only electrons in the outer energy levels are involved in bonding

Covalent bonding

❑ with **covalent bonding** the stable electron arrangements are achieved by the sharing of pairs of electrons between atoms

Examples   **hydrogen chloride**

H   Cl   HCl

nitrogen hydride (ammonia)

H   N   NH₃

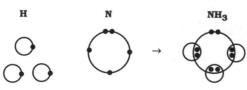

❑ usually only atoms of non-metal elements form covalent bonds

- ❏ it is easier for atoms of elements in Groups 1 to 3 to lose electrons to reach noble gas electron arrangements; this explains why atoms of metal elements do not form covalent bonds

Electron clouds

- ❏ the electrons in the energy levels are arranged in **electron clouds**

- ❏ an electron cloud is a volume of space with a definite shape

- ❏ each electron cloud can hold a maximum of 2 electrons

- ❏ one cloud, shaped like a sphere, makes up the first energy level

- ❏ four clouds, which point towards the corners of a **tetrahedron**, make up the second and third energy levels

- ❏ the clouds which make up the third energy level are bigger and extend further away from the nucleus

- ❏ where possible, each cloud is occupied by a single electron; this decides the way in which the outer electron clouds are filled

Examples

hydrogen   **sulphur**

electron clouds have been "flattened"

- ❏ the merging of half-filled outer electron clouds can be shown by electron sharing diagrams

Examples   **hydrogen sulphide H_2S**

nitrogen chloride   NCl₃

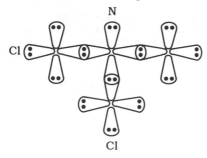

Forces of attraction

❑ the protons give a positive charge to the nucleus of the atom; the electrons give a negative charge to the part of the atom surrounding the nucleus

❑ in a covalent bond the merging of half-filled clouds increases the negative charge in the overlap region

❑ the positive nuclei of both atoms attract the electrons in the overlap region and this holds the atoms together,

   e.g. hydrogen

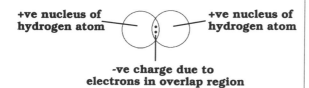

+ve nucleus of hydrogen atom   **+ve nucleus of hydrogen atom**

-ve charge due to electrons in overlap region

+ve <-------------> **-ve** <-------------> **+ve**
   attraction   **attraction**

❑ covalent bonds are strong forces of attraction; a lot of energy is required to break covalent bonds

❑ the bonds between the molecules are weaker than the covalent bonds within molecules   **strong covalent bonds**

   weak bonds between molecules

Polar covalent bonding

❑ pure covalent bonding is only found in elements, i.e. when the bonded atoms are identical so that the bonding electrons are shared equally between the atoms,

e.g. H_2, Cl_2, etc.

❑ in most covalent compounds the bonding is **polar covalent**, i.e. the bonding electrons are not equally shared but are pulled closer to one of the atoms

❑ there are highly polar covalent bonds in water

$$\delta\text{-}O$$
$$\delta\text{+}H \diagup \quad \diagdown H^{\delta\text{+}}$$

δ the Greek letter 'd' means 'very small'

❑ the oxygen atom has a greater pull on the shared electrons

❑ there is therefore a small permanent positive charge on the hydrogen atoms and a small permanent negative charge on the oxygen atom

Discrete covalent substances

❑ a **molecule** is a definite group of atoms held together by covalent bonds

❑ a discrete covalent substance is made up of molecules

❑ a **diatomic** molecule contains two atoms joined together,

e.g. hydrogen (H_2), hydrogen chloride (HCl)

❑ the elements which are made up of diatomic molecules are:

hydrogen	H_2	nitrogen	N_2
oxygen	O_2	fluorine	F_2
chlorine	Cl_2	bromine	Br_2
iodine	I_2		

❑ an oxygen molecule has a double covalent bond;
a nitrogen molecule has a triple covalent bond;
the diatomic molecules of other elements consist of single covalent bonds

❑ the shapes of molecules are based on the tetrahedral arrangement of electrons

Examples

    hydrogen oxide H_2O

    nitrogen hydride NH_3

    carbon tetrachloride CCl_4

❑ the **chemical formula** for a discrete covalent substance gives the number of atoms of each element in a molecule of the substance,

    e.g. hydrogen oxide (H_2O) has two hydrogen atoms and one oxygen atom in each molecule, nitrogen chloride (NCl_3) has one nitrogen atom and three chlorine atoms in each molecule

❑ the **full structural formula** shows the way in which the atoms in a molecule are arranged

Examples   **hydrogen oxide**   **carbon chloride**

$$H \diagup O \diagdown H \qquad Cl-\underset{\underset{Cl}{|}}{\overset{\overset{Cl}{|}}{C}}-Cl$$

❑ chemical formulae can be written from full structural formulae

Examples

$$H-\underset{\underset{H}{|}}{\overset{\overset{H}{|}}{C}}-C\underset{\diagdown OH}{\overset{\diagup\!\!O}{}} \qquad \text{(vinegar)} \qquad C_2H_4O_2$$

$$H-\underset{\underset{OH}{|}}{\overset{\overset{H}{|}}{C}}-\underset{\underset{OH}{|}}{\overset{\overset{H}{|}}{C}}-H \qquad \text{(antifreeze)} \qquad C_2H_6O_2$$

Covalent network structures

☐ a **covalent network structure** consists of a giant lattice of covalently bonded atoms

☐ the chemical formula for a covalent network substance gives the simplest ratio of atoms of each element,

  e.g. silicon dioxide (SiO$_2$) has one silicon atom for every two oxygen atoms

Ionic bonding

☐ **ions** are charged particles formed when atoms lose or gain electrons

☐ ions have the stable arrangements of the atoms of the noble gases

☐ metal atoms lose electrons to form positive ions,

  e.g.

Ion	Charge
sodium	*Na$^+$*
magnesium	*Mg^{2+}*
aluminium	*Al^{3+}*

☐ non-metal atoms gain electrons to form negative ions,

  e.g.

Ion	Charge
chloride	*Cl$^-$*
oxide	*O^{2-}*
nitride	*N^{3-}*

☐ some of the transition metals have ions with more than one charge (see page 26),

  e.g. Cu$^+$, Cu^{2+}

☐ group ions contain more than one kind of atom (see page 27),

  e.g. ammonium (NH$_4^+$), sulphate (SO$_4^{2-}$)

☐ when elements react to form ionic compounds the stable electron arrangement is achieved by the transfer of electrons between atoms

Examples   **sodium fluoride**

Na   **F**   **NaF**

magnesium chloride

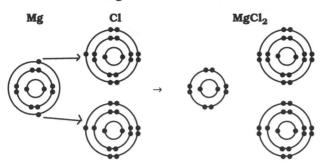

- ionic compounds usually contain metal ions (but note that some ionic compounds contain ammonium ions)

- ionic bonding is the electrostatic force of attraction between oppositely charged ions

- ionic bonds are strong forces of attraction; a lot of energy is required to break ionic bonds

- an **ionic structure** consists of a giant lattice of oppositely charged ions

- the chemical formula for an ionic substance gives the simplest ratio of ions of each element,

  e.g. sodium chloride (NaCl) has one sodium ion for every one chloride ion,
  potassium oxide (K_2O) has two potassium ions for every one oxide ion

Metallic bonding

- atoms in a metal contribute the electrons in their outermost energy levels to a common 'pool' of free or delocalised electrons

- each positively charged ion is attracted to the pool of negative electrons and vice versa; these electrostatic attractions constitute the metallic bonds

nuclei and inner energy level electrons, i.e. positively charged ions

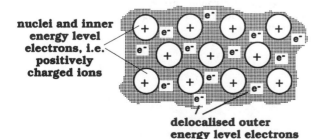

delocalised outer energy level electrons

❑ a lot of energy is required to overcome the forces of attraction; as a result, metallic bonds are strong

❑ a metallic structure consists of a giant lattice of positively charged ions in a sea of delocalised outer electrons

❑ the outer electrons which are contributed to the pool are free to move from one ion to another throughout the metal lattice

❑ the metallic bonds hold the entire metal lattice together as a single unit

Electrical conductivity

❑ electric current is a flow of charged particles; these could be electrons or ions

❑ an **electrical conductor** is a substance which allows electricity to pass through it

❑ metal elements (solids and liquids) and carbon (graphite) are conductors of electricity because they contain free electrons which can flow

❑ the movement of electrons does not chemically change an element

❑ covalent substances (solids, liquids and solutions) do **not** conduct electricity since they are made up of molecules which are uncharged

❑ ionic compounds do **not** conduct electricity in the solid state because the ions are not free to move

❑ ionic compounds conduct electricity when molten or dissolved in water

❑ ions are able to flow through ionic melts and solutions

❑ an ionic compound in solution or as a melt is referred to as an **electrolyte**

❑ the movement of ions through an electrolyte causes chemical reactions to occur at the electrodes leading to the decomposition of the electrolyte

❑ substances can be classified in different ways

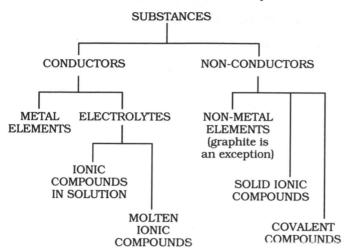

SUBSTANCES

CONDUCTORS   NON-CONDUCTORS

METAL ELEMENTS   ELECTROLYTES   NON-METAL ELEMENTS (graphite is an exception)

IONIC COMPOUNDS IN SOLUTION

SOLID IONIC COMPOUNDS

MOLTEN IONIC COMPOUNDS

COVALENT COMPOUNDS

SUBSTANCES

ELEMENTS   COMPOUNDS

METALS	NON-METALS	IONIC	COVALENT
conduct when solid or molten	do not conduct in any state, carbon (graphite) is an exception	do not conduct when solid, but conduct when molten or in solution	do not conduct in any state, but some ionise in water and then conduct
electrons flow through metals		ions flow through ionic compounds when molten or in solution	
no chemical change		chemical reactions occur at electrodes	

Melting and boiling points

☐ ionic compounds have high melting and boiling points

☐ all ionic compounds are solid at room temperature

☐ covalent network substances have high melting and boiling points

☐ all covalent networks substances are solid at room temperature

☐ discrete covalent substances have low melting and boiling points

☐ discrete covalent substances can be solid at room temperature

☐ substances which exist as liquids or gases at room temperature are discrete covalent substances (but note mercury which is a metal)

☐ substances can be classified as solids, liquids and gases

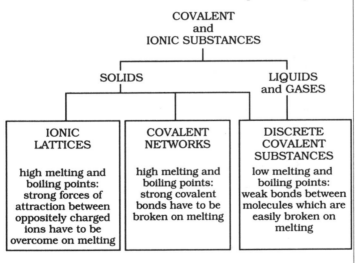

Solubility

See
UNIT 1 PPA 3

❑ ionic compounds usually dissolve in water with the lattice breaking up completely,

 e.g. salt (sodium chloride)

❑ some covalent substances are soluble in water,

 e.g. sugar

❑ covalent substances which are insoluble in water can dissolve in other solvents,

 e.g. paints are soluble in turpentine, nail varnish is soluble in acetone

Electrolysis

❑ electrolysis is the use of electricity to split up an ionic compound in solution or as a melt (an electrolyte)

❑ a direct current (d.c.) supply must be used if the products are to be identified

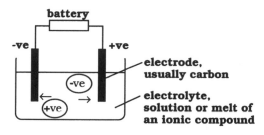

❑ negative non-metal ions are attracted to the positive electrode; positive metal ions are attracted to the negative electrode,

e.g.

Solution/melt	Product at positive electrode	Product at negative electrode
copper chloride solution	chlorine	copper
lead iodide melt	iodine	lead

❑ the non-metal ions lose electrons to form atoms at the positive electrode,

 e.g. $2Cl^-(aq) \rightarrow Cl_2(g) + 2e^-$

❑ the metal ions gain electrons to form atoms at the negative electrode,

 e.g. $Cu^{2+}(aq) + 2e^- \rightarrow Cu(s)$

Colours of ionic compounds

❑ the colours of ionic compounds depend on the colours of the positive and negative ions

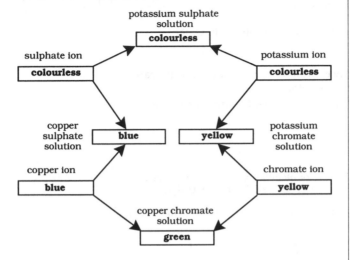

Electrolysis of copper chromate solution

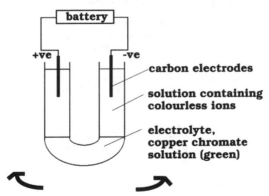

❑ movement of yellow colour towards the positive electrode;

movement of blue colour towards the negative electrode;

❑ chromate ions (negative) are attracted towards this electrode and lose electrons

copper ions (positive) are attracted towards this electrode and gain electrons

5. CHEMICAL SYMBOLISM

Writing formulae - covalent compounds

❑ covalent compounds (usually) are made up of atoms of non-metal elements

❑ the number of bonds which an atom forms is equal to the number of "extra" electrons which an atom requires to reach the same electron arrangement as a noble gas

	C	N	O	F	Ne
	Si	P	S	Cl	Ar

Number of outer electrons	4	5	6	7	8
Number of extra electrons	4	3	2	1	0
Number of bonds formed	4	3	2	1	0

Example   **carbon fluoride**

Step 1   Use the Periodic Table to write symbols for the elements

         C   F

Step 2   Use the Periodic Table to put in the number of bonds which will be formed by each atom

$$-\overset{|}{\underset{|}{C}}- \quad -F$$

Step 3   Complete the bonding picture

$$F-\overset{\overset{\textstyle F}{|}}{\underset{\underset{\textstyle F}{|}}{C}}-F$$

Step 4   Write the formula CF_4

❑ the formulae for some covalent compounds are indicated by the names using prefixes; do not use the Periodic Table for these compounds,
e.g.

Prefix	Meaning	Name	Formula
mono-	1	carbon monoxide	CO
di-	2	carbon dioxide	CO_2
tri-	3	sulphur trioxide	SO_3
tetra-	4	carbon tetrachloride	CCl_4
hexa-	6	uranium hexafluoride	UF_6

Writing formulae - ionic compounds

(a) Simple ionic compounds

❑ ionic compounds contain a metal ion (or the ammonium ion)

❑ the charge on many ions can be worked out from the electron arrangements on page 1 of the Data Booklet

Group 1	Group 2	Group 3	Group 4	Group 5	Group 6	Group 7
1+	2+	3+		3-	2-	1-

❑ in an ionic compound, the charge on all positive ions must balance the charge on all negative ions

❑ the formula for an ionic compound can be worked out by finding the relative number of each ion required to make the overall charge zero

Examples   **sodium chloride**

positive ion   negative ion

Na^+ Cl^-

formula Na^+Cl^- or $NaCl$

potassium oxide

positive ion   negative ion

K^+ O^{2-}

formula $(K^+)_2O^{2-}$ or K_2O

(b) Elements with ions which show variable charge

❑ some metals have ions with more than one charge; in compounds of these metals the charge is shown in Roman numerals after the name of the metal element,

e.g. in iron(II) oxide the charge of the iron is two-positive (Fe^{2+}); in copper(I) oxide the charge of the copper is one-positive (Cu^+)

Example   **copper(I) oxide**

positive ion   negative ion

Cu^+ O^{2-}

formula $(Cu^+)_2O^{2-}$ or Cu_2O

(c) Group ions

❏ a number of ions consist of a group of atoms which tend to stay together during reactions; these are called **group ions**

❏ the charge is on the whole group and not on any particular atom,

e.g. *the sulphate ion*   **the charge of the ion is 2- negative**

$$SO_4^{2-}$$

formula for the ion

❏ the formula and charge of a group ion can be found on page 4 of the Data Booklet

❏ the presence of a group ion can usually be recognised from the -ate or -ite name ending which indicates the presence of oxygen

❏ the exceptions are the ammonium ion and the hydroxide ion

❏ apart from the ammonium ion, which has a positive charge like the metal ions, all the group ions have a negative charge

Example 1   sodium nitrate

positive ion   negative ion

Na^+ NO_3^-

formula $Na^+(NO_3^-)$ or $Na^+NO_3^-$ or $NaNO_3$

Note: Always put the formula for the group ion in brackets. When the subscript numeral for the group is 1, as above, the brackets can be removed. When the subscript numeral for the group is greater than 1, brackets are essential.

Example 2   calcium nitrate

positive ion   negative ion

Ca^{2+} NO_3^-

formula $Ca^{2+}(NO_3^-)_2$ or $Ca(NO_3)_2$

Note: The formula for calcium nitrate is $Ca(NO_3)_2$ and **not** $CaNO_3$ $_2$
The formula has one calcium ion for every two nitrate ions. This gives a ratio of one calcium atom: two nitrogen atoms : six oxygen atoms.

Writing formulae - using combining powers (valency)

❑ the chemical formula for a compound can always be worked out by considering the bonding; there is, however, a shorter method which uses the combining powers (valency); this method works for both covalent and ionic compounds

❑ the combining power can be found from the Periodic Table

Group 1	Group 2	Group 3	Group 4	Group 5	Group 6	Group 7
1	2	3	4	3	2	1

❑ for metals which show variable charge the combining power corresponds to the charge on the ion,

   e.g. in iron(II) oxide the combining power of the iron ion is 2, in copper(I) oxide the combining power of the copper ion is 1

❑ for group ions, the combining power corresponds to the charge on the ion,

   e.g. in $SO_4{}^{2-}$ the combining power of the ion is 2,

   in $NO_3{}^-$ the combining power of the ion is 1

❑ this method will always give the correct answer, but it does not show you why it is correct; use in emergency when all else fails!

Example 1   **hydrogen sulphide**

Step 1   Write atoms and combining   1   2
           powers in this form   H   S

Step 2   Exchange the combining   1   2
           powers   H ✗ S

Step 3   Ignore the number 1 to
           give the correct
           chemical formula H_2S

Example 2   **potassium sulphate**

Step 1   As before   1   2
                                             K SO_4

Step 2   As before   1   2
                                             K ✗ SO_4

Step 3   As before K_2SO_4

An extra step is sometimes necessary.

Example 3   silicon oxide

Step 1	As before	4 2 Si O
Step 2	Cancel the numbers 2 and 4 to give 1 and 2	2 1 Si ✕ O
Step 3	As step 2 before	2 1 Si ✕ O
Step 4	As step 3 before	SiO_2

Balanced equations

❑ in a chemical reaction, substances present at the start change to make new substances

❑ the chemical reaction can be written in a short-hand form, called a **word equation**,

e.g.

```
STARTING SUBSTANCE A  +  STARTING SUBSTANCE  B

                     ↓

NEW SUBSTANCE  C  +  NEW SUBSTANCE  D
```

OR

```
STARTING                NEW SUBSTANCE L
SUBSTANCE  K      →            +
                        NEW SUBSTANCE  M
```

OR

```
STARTING SUBSTANCE X  +  STARTING SUBSTANCE Y

                     ↓

NEW  SUBSTANCE  Z
```

❑ the starting substances in chemical reactions are called the **reactants**; the new substances which are produced are called the **products**

❑ in a word equation:

   (i)   the '+' sign means '**and**'
   (ii) the '→' sign means '**changed into**'
   (iii) the **reactants** come **in front** of the arrow;
         the **products** come **after** the arrow

Example

Here is a chemical reaction from everyday life.

The food in our bodies joins up with oxygen taken from the air to produce water vapour and carbon dioxide which we breathe out.

The word equation is:

food + oxygen → water vapour + carbon dioxide
   the reactants   **the products**

Equations using symbols and formulae

❑ an equation using symbols and formulae gives more information than a word equation - it shows the elements involved and the way in which they are joined up in the reactant(s) and product(s)

Example

The word equation for the burning of natural gas is:

natural gas + oxygen → carbon dioxide + water

This equation can be written using the formula for each reactant and product:

$$CH_4 \ + \ O_2 \ \rightarrow \ CO_2 \ + \ H_2O$$

❑ in a reaction the atoms which take part (either as an element or as part of a compound) also make up what is formed

❑ the following flow diagram can be used when writing equations; it should be followed for each substance in the equation in turn

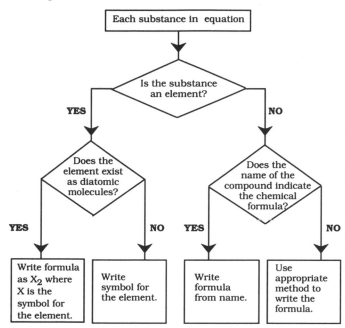

Balanced chemical equations

❑ the number of atoms (or ions) on the reactant side is equal to the number of atoms (or ions) on the product side

Example

The balanced chemical equation for the burning of magnesium is:

$$2Mg \; + \; O_2 \; \rightarrow \; 2MgO$$

❑ equations can only be balanced by putting a number in front of symbols and formulae,

e.g. **2Mg** or **2MgO**

❑ never change a formula to make an equation balance,

e.g. *the formula for carbon dioxide is always CO_2*
(CO is carbon monoxide, a quite different gas),
the formula for water is always H_2O
(HO does not exist)

❏ the following example shows a method of balancing equations

Example N_2 + H_2 → NH_3

N		H		NH
N	+	H	→	H
				H

Two nitrogens are required on the product side.

N		H		NH
N	+	H	→	H
				H
				NH
				H
				H

Six hydrogens are required on the reactant side.

N		H		NH
N	+	H	→	H
				H
		H		
		H		NH
		H		H
		H		H

$$N_2 + 3H_2 → 2NH_3$$

State symbols

❏ state symbols can be used in equations

Example

The word equation for the burning of hydrogen is:

   hydrogen gas + oxygen gas → liquid water

The word equation with state symbols is:

   hydrogen (g) + oxygen (g) → water (l)

or, using symbols and formulae:

   $2H_2(g)$ + $O_2(g)$ → $2H_2O(l)$

6. THE MOLE

Relative formula mass

❑ the mass of an atom is very small when grams is the unit which is used

❑ the mass of an atom is measured on the atomic mass scale and the basic unit is the atomic mass unit (amu)

❑ the masses of atoms given on page 4 of the Data Booklet are given as **relative atomic masses**; no units are required since the scale is relative to the mass of other atoms,

e.g. *an atom of helium (relative atomic mass 4) is four times as heavy as an atom of hydrogen (relative atomic mass 1)*

❑ the relative mass of a 'unit' of a compound is called the **relative formula mass**

❑ the relative formula mass is obtained by adding together all the atomic masses of the atoms (or ions) in the formula

Example

What is the formula mass of sodium carbonate?

Step 1	Write the formula	Na_2CO_3			*you may have to work this out*
Step 2	Find the relative atomic masses	Na 23	C 12	O 16	*use the Data Booklet*
Step 3	Multiply by the number of atoms/ions	23x2	12x1	16x3	*check with the formula*
Step 4	Do the sum	46 + 12 + 48			*calculator?*
Step 5	The answer	**106**			*check it!*

The mole

❑   one **mole** of any substance is defined as the relative formula mass in grams, i.e. the gram formula mass

❑   the relative formula mass of any substance is first calculated from the formula

❑   to calculate the mass of one mole of the substance, simply use grams as the unit

Example 1

What is the mass of one mole of sodium?

Step 1	Symbol	Na
Step 2	Find the relative atomic mass	23
Step 3	Use grams as the unit	**23 g**

Example 2

What is the mass of one mole of sodium sulphate?

Step 1	Write the formula	Na_2SO_4		
Step 2	Find the relative atomic masses	Na 23	S 32	O 16
Step 3	Multiply by the number of atoms/ions	23x2	32x1	16x4
Step 4	Do the sum	46 + 32 + 64		
Step 5	Relative formula mass	142		
Step 6	Use grams as the unit	**142 g**		

Example 3

What is the mass of two moles of sodium chloride?

Step 1	Write the formula	NaCl	
Step 2	Find the relative atomic masses	Na 23	Cl 35.5
Step 3	Multiply by the number of atoms/ions	23x1	35.5x1
Step 4	Do the sum	23 + 35.5	
Step 5	Relative formula mass	58.5	
Step 6	Use grams as the unit	58.5 g	
Step 7	Complete calculation	1 mol $\longleftrightarrow$ 58.5 g	
		2 mol $\longleftrightarrow$ **117 g**	

❑ the $\longleftrightarrow$ symbol is used to show a simple proportion

Example 4

How many moles are there in 36 g of water?

Step 1	Write the formula	H_2O	
Step 2	Find the relative atomic masses	H 1	O 16
Step 3	Multiply by the number of atoms/ions	1x2	16x1
Step 4	Do the sum	2 + 16	
Step 5	Relative formula mass	18	
Step 6	Use grams as the unit	18 g	
Step 7	Complete calculation	18 g $\longleftrightarrow$ 1 mol	
		36 g $\longleftrightarrow$ **2 mol**	

Using balanced equations

❑ a balanced equation can be taken to give the **relative number of moles** of each reactant and product

❑ since the mass of one mole of any substance is expressed in grams, the masses involved can then be calculated

Example 1

Calculate the mass of water produced on burning 1 g of methane.

Step 1	Balanced equation	CH_4 + $2O_2$ → CO_2 + $2H_2O$

Step 2	Relative number of moles	1 mol	2 mol

❑ it is not necessary to calculate the masses of carbon dioxide and oxygen - these substances are not included in the question

		CH_4	$2H_2O$
Step 3	Find the relative formula masses	12 + (4x1)	2[((2x1) + 16)]
		= 16	= 36
Step 4	Mass in grams	16 g	36 g
Step 5	Complete calculation	16 g ↔ 36 g	
		1 g ↔ $\frac{36 \times 1}{16}$	

$$= \textbf{2.25 g}$$

Example 2

An industrial plant produces ammonia by the Haber Process.
An output of 7.5×10^3 kg of ammonia is required each day.
Calculate the mass of nitrogen used each day.

Step 1	Balanced equation	N_2 + $3H_2$ → $2NH_3$

Step 2	Relative number of moles	1 mol	2 mol
Step 3	Find the relative formula masses	2x14	2[14 + (3x1)]
		= 28	= 34
Step 4	Mass in grams	= 28 g	= 34 g
Step 5	Complete calculation	28 g ↔ 34 g	
		$\frac{28 \times 7.5 \times 10^3}{34}$ ↔ 7.5×10^3 g	

$$= \textbf{6.18} \times \textbf{10}^3 \textbf{ kg}$$

Unit 2 — Carbon Compounds

1. FUELS

Combustion

□ a **fuel** is a chemical which is burned to produce energy (usually heat)

□ when a substance burns it reacts with **oxygen**

□ **combustion** is another word for burning

□ a chemical reaction in which energy is produced is called an **exothermic** reaction

Hydrocarbons

□ **hydrocarbons** are compounds of hydrogen and carbon only,

  e.g. butane, C_4H_{10}, is a hydrocarbon but acetone, C_2H_6O is not

□ the carbon compounds which are found in oil and natural gas are mainly **hydrocarbons**

□ when a hydrocarbon burns in a plentiful supply of air, the hydrogen and carbon combine with oxygen to produce water and carbon dioxide; this is called **complete combustion**

□ the test for carbon dioxide is that it turns lime water (calcium hydroxide solution) milky

□ hydrocarbons can be burned in the laboratory and the products identified

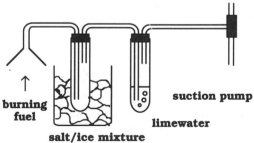

burning fuel

salt/ice mixture

limewater

suction pump

□ if the limewater turns milky, carbon dioxide must be produced; the fuel must contain carbon

❑ if a colourless liquid collects in the tube surrounded by the salt/ice mixture the boiling point and freezing point can be taken; if the liquid boils at 100 °C and freezes at 0 °C water must be produced; the fuel must contain hydrogen

Pollution problems

❑ when a hydrocarbon burns in air with insufficient oxygen for complete combustion carbon and carbon monoxide can be produced

❑ carbon monoxide is a poisonous gas which combines with haemoglobin in the blood

❑ sulphur compounds in some fossil fuels burn to produce sulphur dioxide, a poisonous gas, which is very soluble in water

❑ solutions of sulphur dioxide in water contribute to the acid rain problem

❑ removing sulphur compounds from fuels reduces air pollution

❑ in petrol engines, the electrical spark provides enough energy to cause the nitrogen to react with the oxygen of the air to form oxides of nitrogen; these poisonous gases also dissolve in water to produce acidic solutions

❑ the incomplete combustion of diesel can produce soot particles which are harmful

❑ air pollution from the combustion of hydrocarbons can be reduced by the use of catalytic converters which speed up conversion of pollutant gases to harmless gases

❑ carbon monoxide and oxides of nitrogen can react to produce carbon dioxide and nitrogen

Fractional distillation

❑ **crude oil** is the mixture of chemical compounds, mainly hydrocarbons

❑ **fractional distillation** is the process used to separate the different hydrocarbons in crude oil according to their boiling points

❑ a group of hydrocarbons with similar boiling points within a given range is called a **fraction**,

e.g. *petroleum gas, gasoline, kerosine, gas oils, residue*

	Petroleum gas	Gasoline (naphtha)	Kerosine	Gas oils	Residue
Number of carbon atoms	1 - 4	5 - 10	11 - 12	13 - 25	25+
Ease of evaporation	←	easier to evaporate			
Viscosity		becoming thicker			→
Flammability	←	easier to ignite			
Boiling point range / °C	-160 to 20	20 to 120	120 to 240	240 to 350	over 350
Examples of use	calor gas fuel	petrol fuel	jet aircraft fuel, paraffin for lamps	diesel fuel	lubricants, waxes, road tar

❑   as molecular size increases the boiling point increases (stronger forces between different molecules)

❑   as molecular size increases flammability decreases (less likely to be a vapour)

❑   as molecular size increases viscosity increases (longer molecules become tangled up)

2. NOMENCLATURE AND STRUCTURAL FORMULAE

Alkanes

❑ the **alkanes** are a subset of the set of hydrocarbons

❑ each member of the alkane series has a name which ends in **-ane** and a prefix which indicates the number of carbon atoms in the molecule

Prefix	Number of C atoms	Prefix	Number of C atoms
meth-	1	pent-	5
eth-	2	hex-	6
prop-	3	hept-	7
but-	4	oct-	8

❑ all alkanes are **saturated** hydrocarbons, i.e. all the carbon to carbon bonds are single covalent bonds

❑ the **full structural formula** can be used to show the arrangement of atoms; a **shortened structural** formula can be used to show the grouping of hydrogen atoms round each carbon,

e.g.

1
methane

$$H-\overset{\displaystyle H}{\underset{\displaystyle H}{C}}-H$$

CH_4
CH_4

KEY
Number of carbon atoms
Name
Full structural formula
Shortened structural formula
Molecular formula

2
ethane

$$H-\overset{\displaystyle H}{\underset{\displaystyle H}{C}}-\overset{\displaystyle H}{\underset{\displaystyle H}{C}}-H$$

CH_3-CH_3
C_2H_6

3
propane

$$H-\overset{\displaystyle H}{\underset{\displaystyle H}{C}}-\overset{\displaystyle H}{\underset{\displaystyle H}{C}}-\overset{\displaystyle H}{\underset{\displaystyle H}{C}}-H$$

$CH_3-CH_2-CH_3$
C_3H_8

4
butane

$$H-\overset{\displaystyle H}{\underset{\displaystyle H}{C}}-\overset{\displaystyle H}{\underset{\displaystyle H}{C}}-\overset{\displaystyle H}{\underset{\displaystyle H}{C}}-\overset{\displaystyle H}{\underset{\displaystyle H}{C}}-H$$

$CH_3-CH_2-CH_2-CH_3$
C_4H_{10}

5
pentane

$$H-\overset{\displaystyle H}{\underset{\displaystyle H}{C}}-\overset{\displaystyle H}{\underset{\displaystyle H}{C}}-\overset{\displaystyle H}{\underset{\displaystyle H}{C}}-\overset{\displaystyle H}{\underset{\displaystyle H}{C}}-\overset{\displaystyle H}{\underset{\displaystyle H}{C}}-H$$

$CH_3-CH_2-CH_2-CH_2-CH_3$
C_5H_{12}

6	7
hexane	heptane

$$CH_3\text{-}CH_2\text{-}CH_2\text{-}CH_2\text{-}CH_2\text{-}CH_3$$
$$C_6H_{14}$$

$$CH_3\text{-}CH_2\text{-}CH_2\text{-}CH_2\text{-}CH_2\text{-}CH_2\text{-}CH_3$$
$$C_7H_{16}$$

8

octane

$$CH_3\text{-}CH_2\text{-}CH_2\text{-}CH_2\text{-}CH_2\text{-}CH_2\text{-}CH_2\text{-}CH_3$$
$$C_8H_{18}$$

❑ the general formula for the alkanes is C_nH_{2n+2} where n is the number of carbon atoms

Alkenes

❑ the **alkenes** are also a subset of the set of hydrocarbons

❑ each member of the alkene series has a name which ends in **-ene** and a prefix which indicates the number of carbon atoms in the molecule

❑ all alkenes are **unsaturated** hydrocarbons, i.e. there is at least one carbon to carbon double bond,

e.g.

2

ethene

$$CH_2=CH_2$$
$$C_2H_4$$

KEY

Number of carbon atoms
Name
Full structural formula
Shortened structural formula
Molecular formula

3

propene

$$CH_3\text{-}CH=CH_2$$
$$C_3H_6$$

4

butene

$$CH_3\text{-}CH_2\text{-}CH=CH_2$$
$$C_4H_8$$

5 pentene	6 hexene

5
pentene

H−C−C−C−C=C (with H atoms: H H H H on top, H H H below, H and H on right)

$CH_3\text{-}CH_2\text{-}CH_2\text{-}CH=CH_2$

C_5H_{10}

6
hexene

H−C−C−C−C−C=C (with H atoms: H H H H H on top, H H H H below, H and H on right)

$CH_3\text{-}CH_2\text{-}CH_2\text{-}CH_2\text{-}CH=CH_2$

C_6H_{12}

❑ the carbon to carbon double bond is an example of a **functional group**, i.e. a group of atoms with characteristic properties

❑ the general formula for the alkenes is C_nH_{2n} (each alkene has two hydrogens less than the corresponding alkane due to the double bond)

Cycloalkanes

❑ alkanes with a ring of carbon atoms are called **cycloalkanes**

❑ the cycloalkanes are also a subset of the set of hydrocarbons

❑ each member of the series has a name which ends in **-ane** and a prefix which starts with cyclo and indicates the number of carbon atoms in the molecule

❑ all cycloalkanes are also **saturated** hydrocarbons, i.e. they contain only carbon to carbon atoms,

e.g.

3
cyclopropane

H   H
 \ /
  C
 / \
H−C−C−H
  | |
  H   H

CH_2
$CH_2\text{-}CH_2$

C_3H_6

KEY
Number of carbon atoms
Name
Full structural formula
Shortened structural formula
Molecular formula

4

cyclobutane

$$H-\underset{\underset{H}{|}}{\overset{\overset{H}{|}}{C}}-\underset{\underset{H}{|}}{\overset{\overset{H}{|}}{C}}-H$$
$$H-\underset{\underset{H}{|}}{\overset{\overset{}{|}}{C}}-\underset{\underset{H}{|}}{\overset{\overset{}{|}}{C}}-H$$

$$\underset{CH_2-CH_2}{\overset{CH_2-CH_2}{|\qquad|}}$$

$$C_4H_8$$

5

cyclopentane

$$CH_2$$
$$CH_2 \qquad CH_2$$
$$CH_2-CH_2$$

$$C_5H_{10}$$

6

cyclohexane

$$CH_2-CH_2$$
$$CH_2 \qquad CH_2$$
$$CH_2-CH_2$$

$$C_6H_{12}$$

- the general formula for the cycloalkanes is also C_nH_{2n}
  (each cycloalkane has two hydrogens less than the corresponding alkane due to the closing of the chain)

Homologous series

- a **homologous series** is a family of compounds which can be represented by a general formula,
  e.g. the alkanes (C_nH_{2n+2}) and the alkenes (C_nH_{2n})

- successive members in a series differ in formula by a CH_2 group and hence relative molecular masses differ by 14

- there is a gradual change from one member of a homologous series to the next in physical properties,
  e.g. boiling point

- chemical properties of compounds in a homologous series are very similar due to all members having the same functional group,
  e.g. the reaction of the alkenes with bromine

Straight and branched chains

❑ in a **straight** chain all the carbon atoms are joined to one (at end) or two neighbouring carbon atoms,

  e.g. $CH_3-CH_2-CH_2-CH_2-CH_3$

❑ in a **branched** chain one or more of the carbon atoms may be joined to three or four neighbouring carbon atoms,

  e.g. $CH_3-\underset{\underset{CH_3}{|}}{CH}-CH_2-CH_3$ $CH_3-\underset{\underset{CH_3}{|}}{\overset{\overset{CH_3}{|}}{C}}-CH_3$

❑ branches are names after the corresponding alkanes with the -ane ending changed to -yl,

  e.g.

  CH_3 — **a methyl branch**

  C_3H_7 — **a propyl branch**

Systematic naming

❑ organic chemicals are given a systematic name according to an internationally accepted convention

❑ **to name a branched-chain alkane**

  (i) select the longest continous chain of carbon atoms and name it after the appropriate straight-chain alkane

  (ii) number the carbon atoms from the end of the chain nearer the branch

  (iii) name the branch(es) and indicate the position(s) of the branch(es) on the chain,

  e.g.

  $\underset{4\quad\ 3\quad\ 2\quad 1}{CH_3-CH_2-\underset{\underset{CH_3}{|}}{CH}-CH_3}$ **2-methylbutane**
  NOT
  3-methylbutane

  $\overset{1}{\underset{2}{\ }}\ \overset{CH_3}{\underset{CH_2-CH-CH_2-CH_3}{|}}$ with positions 3 4 5 and $\underset{CH_3}{|}$

  3-methylpentane
  NOT
  1,2-dimethylbutane

  $\overset{1}{\ }CH_3$
  $\overset{2}{\ }CH_2$
  $CH_3-CH-CH_2-CH_3$

  3-methylpentane
  NOT
  2-ethylbutane

❑ cycloalkanes are named in a similar way,

e.g. **methylcyclobutane**   **1,3-dimethylcyclohexane**

$$CH_3$$
$$|$$
$$H_2C - CH$$
$$| \quad |$$
$$H_2C - CH_2$$

$$CH_2 \ \mathbf{3}$$
$$CH_2 \quad CH - CH_3$$
$$| \qquad |$$
$$CH_2 \quad CH_2$$
$$\mathbf{1} \ \ CH \ \mathbf{2}$$
$$|$$
$$CH_3$$

❑ **to name an alkene**

(i) select the longest continous chain of carbon atoms containing the double bond and name it after the appropriate straight-chain alkene

(ii) number the carbon atoms from the end of the chain nearer the double bond and indicate the position of the double bond

(iii) name any branch(es) and indicate the position(s) of the branch(es) on the chain,

e.g. $CH_3\text{-}CH_2\text{-}CH\text{=}CH_2$ $CH_3\text{-}CH\text{=}CH\text{-}CH_3$
       4   **3**   **2**   **1**   **1**   **2**   **3**   **4**
       but-1-ene   **but-2-ene**

$$CH_3$$
$$|$$
$$CH_2\text{=}CH\text{-}CH\text{-}CH_3\text{-}CH_3$$
1   **2**   **3**   **4**   **5**
3-methylpent-1-ene

Isomers

❏ **isomers** are compounds with the same molecular formula but different structures

❏ the following flow diagram can be used to decide whether or not two compounds are isomers

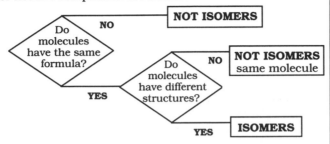

Examples

CH_3-CH_2-CH_3 CH_3-CH_3

    A   **B**

these compounds have **different formulae**; they are **NOT** isomers; **A** is propane **B** is ethane

$\begin{array}{c} CH_3 \\ | \\ CH_3\text{-}CH\text{-}CH_2\text{-}CH_3 \end{array}$ $\begin{array}{c} CH_3\text{-}CH_2\text{-}CH\text{-}CH_3 \\ | \\ CH_3 \end{array}$

    C   **D**

these compounds have the **same formula** and the **same structure**; they are **NOT** isomers; they are both 2-methylbutane

$\begin{array}{c} CH_3 \\ | \\ CH_3\text{-}C\text{-}CH_3 \\ | \\ CH_3 \end{array}$ $\begin{array}{c} CH_3\text{-}CH\text{-}CH_2\text{-}CH_3 \\ | \\ CH_3 \end{array}$

    E   **F**

these compounds have the **same formula** but have **different structures**; they are isomers; **E** is 2,2-dimethylpropane **F** is 2-methylbutane

CH_2=CH-CH_2-CH_3 CH_3-CH=CH-CH_3

    G   **H**

these compounds have the **same formula** but have **different structures**; they are isomers; **G** is but-1-ene **H** is but-2-ene

$\begin{array}{c} CH_2\text{=}C\text{-}CH_3 \\ | \\ CH_3 \end{array}$ $\begin{array}{c} CH_2\text{—}CH_2 \\ | \quad\quad | \\ CH_2\text{—}CH_2 \end{array}$

    I   **J**

these compounds have the **same formula** but have **different structures**; they are isomers, even though one compound is an alkene and the other a cycloalkane; **I** is methylpropene **J** is cyclobutane

❏ many compounds, other than hydrocarbons, have isomers,

Examples

$CH_3\text{-}CH\text{-}CH_3$
    |
    Cl

$CH_3\text{-}CH_2\text{-}CH_2Cl$

these compounds have the **same formula** but have **different structures**; they are isomers

$$\begin{array}{c} \text{Cl H} \\ |\ \ | \\ \text{H-C}\!-\!\text{C-H} \\ |\ \ | \\ \text{H Cl} \end{array}$$

$$\begin{array}{c} \text{H H} \\ |\ \ | \\ \text{Cl-C}\!-\!\text{C-Cl} \\ |\ \ | \\ \text{H H} \end{array}$$

these compounds have the **same formula**;they also have the **same structure** although the full structural formulae is drawn in different ways; they are **NOT** isomers

$$\begin{array}{c} \text{Cl H} \\ |\ \ | \\ \text{H-C}\!-\!\text{C-H} \\ |\ \ | \\ \text{H Cl} \end{array}$$

$$\begin{array}{c} \text{Cl H} \\ |\ \ | \\ \text{Cl-C}\!-\!\text{C-H} \\ |\ \ | \\ \text{H H} \end{array}$$

these compounds have the **same formula** but have **different structures**; they are isomers

Alkanols

❏ ethanol (found in alcoholic drinks) is the second member of a homologous series called the **alkanols**

❏ the alkanols are a subset of the set of **alcohols**

❏ the **hydroxyl** group (**-OH**) is the functional group in the alcohols

❏ each member has a name which ends in **-anol** and a prefix which indicates the number of carbon atoms in the molecule,

e.g.

1
methanol
H
|
H-C-OH
|
H
CH_3OH
CH_4O

KEY
Number of carbon atoms
Name
Full structural formula
Shortened structural formula
Molecular formula

2
ethanol
H H
| |
H-C—C-OH
| |
H H
$CH_3\text{-}CH_2OH$
C_2H_6O

3
propanol
H H H
| | |
H-C—C—C-OH
| | |
H H H
$CH_3\text{-}CH_2\text{-}CH_2OH$
C_3H_8O

❑ from propanol onwards, isomerism can occur due to different positions of the hydroxyl group,

e.g.
$$\overset{3}{C}H_3-\overset{2}{C}H_2-\overset{1}{C}H_2-OH \qquad \overset{1}{C}H_3-\overset{2}{\underset{|}{C}H}-\overset{3}{C}H_3$$
$$\qquad\qquad\qquad\qquad\qquad\qquad OH$$

Naming alkanols

❑ (i) select the longest continous chain of carbon atoms containing the hydroxyl group and name it after the appropriate alkanol;

(ii) number the carbon atoms from the end of the chain nearer the functional group and indicate the position of the functional group;

(iii) name any branch(es) and indicate the position(s) of the branch(es) on the chain,

e.g.
$$\overset{3}{C}H_3-\overset{2}{C}H_2-\overset{1}{C}H_2-OH \qquad \overset{1}{C}H_3-\overset{2}{\underset{|}{C}H}-\overset{3}{C}H_3$$

propan-1-ol $\qquad\qquad\qquad\qquad$ OH $\quad$ **propan-2-ol**

$$\overset{4}{C}H_3-\overset{3}{\underset{|}{C}H}-\overset{2}{C}H_2-\overset{1}{C}H_2-OH \qquad \textbf{3-methylbutan-1-ol}$$
$$\qquad\quad CH_3$$

❑ some alkanols have more than one hydroxyl group,

e.g.
$$\underset{|}{C}H_2-\underset{|}{C}H_2 \qquad\qquad \underset{|}{C}H_2-\underset{|}{C}H-\underset{|}{C}H_2$$
$$OH \quad OH \qquad\qquad\quad OH \quad OH \quad OH$$

ethane-1,2-diol $\qquad\qquad$ **propane-1,2,3-triol**
(ethylene glycol, $\qquad\qquad\qquad$ (glycerol)
found in antifreeze)

Alkanoic acids

❑ ethanoic acid (found in vinegar) is the second member of a homologous series called the **alkanoic acids**

❑ alkanoic acids are a subset of the set of **carboxylic acids**

❑ the functional group in carboxylic acids is the **carboxyl**

group $\left(-C\overset{\displaystyle O}{\underset{\displaystyle OH}{}} \right)$

❑ the functional group must always be at the end of a carbon chain

- each member has a name which ends in -**anoic acid** and a prefix which indicates the member of carbon atoms in the molecule,

e.g.

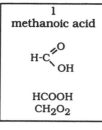

1
methanoic acid
H-C$\stackrel{O}{_{OH}}$
HCOOH
CH_2O_2

KEY
Number of carbon atoms
Name
Full structural formula
Shortened structural formula
Molecular formula

2
ethanoic acid
CH$_3$-COOH
$C_2H_4O_2$

3
propanoic acid
CH$_3$-CH$_2$-COOH
$C_3H_6O_2$

Esters

- esters are covalent compounds with the molecules containing carbon, hydrogen and oxygen atoms

- esters have characteristic smells and are insoluble in water

- esters are the products of reactions between carboxylic acids and alcohols,

  e.g. *the reaction between ethanoic acid and methanol can be represented:*

  CH$_3$-C$\stackrel{O}{_{OH}}$ - - - - - - - - - - - - - - - H$\!$O—CH$_3$

  Note that the structure of the alkanol has been turned round

  acid : ethanoic acid   **alkanol : methanol**

  ⇅

  ester   CH$_3$-C$\stackrel{O}{_{O—CH_3}}$ +   H$_2$O

- since two reactants join up with the elimination of the elements to make water, the making of an ester is an example of a **condensation** reaction; the reaction is also referred to as **esterification**

- the ' ⇌ ' sign shows that the making of an ester is a reversible reaction which can eventually reach equilibrium

❑ an ester takes its name from the alkanol and alkanoic acid from which it can be made,

e.g. alkanol : methanol   acid : ethanoic

       ester : **methyl**   ester : **ethanoate**

name : **methyl ethanoate**

structure :

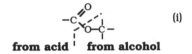

         from acid   from alkanol

❑ since esters are prepared from alcohols and carboxylic acids, all esters contain the functional group:

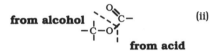

         (i)

      from acid   from alcohol

❑ when written the other way round, the functional group looks like:

from alcohol
$$-\overset{|}{\underset{|}{C}}-O \quad \overset{O}{\underset{}{\parallel}} C-$$
(ii)

         from acid

❑ esters can be represented in short as:

e.g.

    $CH_3C\ O\ OC_2H_5$ (i) $C_2H_5\ O\ OC\ CH_3$ (ii)

  from acid   from alkanol   from alkanol   from acid

❑ esters can be named from their structure,

e.g.   **from alkanol**   **from acid**

$$CH_3-CH_2-O \quad \overset{O}{\underset{}{\parallel}} C-CH_2-CH_3$$

    alkanol : ethanol   acid : propanoic

    ester : **ethyl**   ester : **propanoate**

name : **ethyl propanoate**

3. REACTIONS OF CARBON COMPOUNDS

Addition reactions

See
UNIT 2 PPA 1

❑ alkenes immediately decolourise bromine solution

❑ in the reaction of an alkene with bromine, the double bond breaks open and the two bromine atoms add on to the carbons on either side,

e.g.

propene

❑ this is called an **addition reaction**

❑ alkenes undergo addition reactions with hydrogen to form the corresponding alkanes,

e.g.

butene   **butane**

❑ alkenes undergo addition reactions with hydrogen halides,

e.g.

ethene   **chloroethane**

❑ alkenes have at least one carbon to carbon double bond; the addition reactions of alkenes are a result of this functional group

❑ alkanes and cycloalkanes do **not** undergo addition reactions

Cracking

See
UNIT 2 PPA 2

❑ the process of fractional distillation of crude oil yields more long-chain hydrocarbons than are required to meet present-day demands

❑ **cracking** is an industrial process which breaks up (cracks) the surplus of the heavier fractions, producing a mixture of smaller, more useful molecules,

e.g. for petrol

❑ when a catalyst is used to bring this about, the process is called **catalytic cracking**

- the catalyst allows the reaction to take place at a lower temperature

- catalytic cracking can be carried out in the laboratory

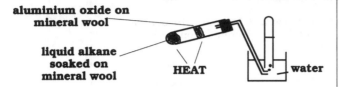

aluminium oxide on mineral wool

liquid alkane soaked on mineral wool

HEAT   **water**

- to avoid 'suckback', the mouth of the delivery tube must be removed from the water before heating is stopped

- since all of the carbon to carbon bonds are equally strong cracking always produces a mixture of products, some of which are saturated and some of which are unsaturated,

  e.g. $C_{24}H_{50}$ $\rightarrow$ $C_{12}H_{24}$ + $C_{12}H_{26}$

  $\rightarrow$ C_6H_{12} + $C_{18}H_{38}$

  $\rightarrow$ C_4H_8 + C_6H_{12} + $C_{14}H_{30}$

- in any one reaction the total numbers of carbon and hydrogen atoms in the product molecules always add up to the total numbers of carbon and hydogen atoms in the reactant molecule

Fermentation

- ethanol, for alcoholic drinks, can be made by **fermentation** of glucose; carbon dioxide gas is produced in the process

- the glucose can come from any fruit or vegetable which is a source of starch or sugars

- the type of alcoholic drink varies with the plant source of the carbohydrate

Source	Drink
grape	wine
barley	beer, whisky
apples	cider
potatoes	vodka

- an enzyme in yeast acts a a catalyst for the reaction

- [ ] at concentrations above about 15% the alcohol poisons the living organisms in the yeast; there is therefore a limit to the alcohol concentration of fermentation products

- [ ] **distillation** is a method of increasing the alcohol concentration of fermentation products in the manufacture of 'spirit' drinks,

  e.g. gin, vodka, whisky

- [ ] water and alcohol can be separated by distillation because of the difference in boiling points; alcohol (bp 78 °C) boils off first

- [ ] different drinks have a different alcohol content

Drink	Alcohol content
beer	4%
wine	10%
spirits	40%

- [ ] alcohol is a sedative and slows down the nervous system; this can lead to loss of control and balance and unconsciousness; death can result

- [ ] long term abuse of alcohol can cause cirrhosis of the liver

- [ ] ethanol is being mixed with petrol for use as an engine fuel in countries where it can be economically produced in sufficient quantities,

  e.g. in Brazil

- [ ] the ethanol can be obtained by the fermentation of sugar cane which can be considered as a renewable source of energy

Production of alcohol

- [ ] to meet market demand, ethanol is made by methods other than fermentation; one industrial method involves the addition of water to ethene using a catalyst

$$\begin{array}{ccc} \overset{H}{\underset{H}{>}}C=C\overset{H}{\underset{H}{<}} & H\text{-}OH & \xrightarrow{\textbf{catalyst}} & H\text{-}\overset{\overset{H}{|}}{\underset{\underset{H}{|}}{C}}\text{-}\overset{\overset{H}{|}}{\underset{\underset{H}{|}}{C}}\text{-}OH \\ \textbf{ethene} & \textbf{water} & & \textbf{ethanol} \end{array}$$

- [ ] this kind of reaction is called **catalytic hydration** or addition; the elements from water add on to the **one** molecule

Dehydration of alcohols

❑ ethanol can be converted to ethene by **dehydration**; the elements to make water come from **one** molecule

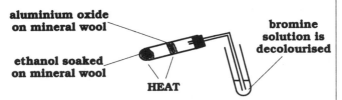

❑ this reaction which is the reverse of hydration, can be carried out in the laboratory

aluminium oxide on mineral wool

ethanol soaked on mineral wool

HEAT

bromine solution is decolourised

❑ butan-1-ol is dehydrated to produce only but-1-ene

```
   H  H  H  H                    H  H       H
   |  |  |  |                    |  |      /
H-C -C -C -C -OH    →     H-C -C -C=C
   |  |  |  |                    |  |  |    \
   H  H  H  H                    H  H  H     H
```
butan-1-ol   **but-1-ene**

❑ butan-2-ol is dehydrated to produce **both** but-1-ene and but-2-ene

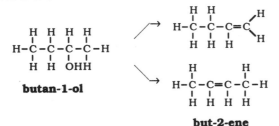

butan-1-ol

```
        H  H       H
        |  |      /
 H-C -C -C=C
        |  |  |    \
        H  H  H     H
```

```
   H              H
   |              |
H-C -C=C -C -H
   |  |  |  |
   H  H  H  H
```
but-2-ene

Making and breaking of esters

❑ the making of an ester is an example of a **condensation** reaction

❑ in the reverse reaction, esters can be broken down to the alcohol and carboxylic acid by heating with an acid or an alkali,

e.g.

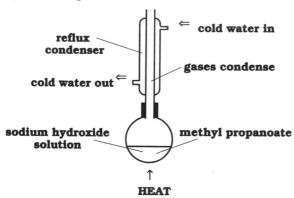

ester : methyl propanoate

condensation ⇅ **hydrolysis**

acid : propanoic acid   **alkanol : methanol**

❑ since the breakdown of the ester occurs due to the addition of the elements of water, this is an example of a **hydrolysis** reaction

❑ the breakdown of an ester is also a reversible reaction which can eventually reach equilibrium

❑ an alkali is normally used to break down an ester in the laboratory,

e.g. sodium hydroxide solution

reflux condenser

⇐ **cold water in**

gases condense

cold water out ⇐

sodium hydroxide solution

methyl propanoate

↑
HEAT

❑ the alkanol can be separated from the acid by **fractional distillation**

4.   PLASTICS AND SYNTHETIC FIBRES

Uses

❑   **synthetic** materials are made by the chemical industry, i.e. they are **not** natural

❑   plastics are examples of synthetic materials,

   e.g. polythene, polystyrene, perspex, PVC, nylon, bakelite, formica and silicones

❑   examples of synthetic fibres include nylon and polyesters,

   e.g. terylene

❑   most plastics and synthetic fibres are made from chemicals obtained from oil

❑   the everyday uses of plastics are related to their properties,

   e.g.

Plastic	Property	Use
PVC	flexible, non-conductor of electricity	insulating electrical cable
PVC	light, does not react with water nor acid rain	house pipes, guttering, window frames
polystyrene	light, poor conductor of heat	packaging, ceiling tiles, drinking cups
poly(ethene)	light, durable, unreactive	washing-up bottles, kitchen bowls

- some recently developed plastics have more unusual properties,

e.g.

Plastic	Property	Use
Kevlar	very strong	to replace steel in cords of car tyres and in ropes for making bullet-proof vests to make protective suits for racing motorcyclists as a lining in aircraft holds to protect an aircraft from an explosion (presently being investigated)
poly(ethenol)	readily dissolves in water	to make laundry bags for hospitals (the bag dissolves when it is placed in hot water and the washing is released which means that hospital workers do not need to handle the dirty linen, reducing the risk of infection) as stitches in surgery (the soluble thread dissolves) to make the protective coatings which cover new cars for the delivery period (the poly(ethenol) can be 'hosed off')

- plastics have replaced many traditional materials,

e.g.

Use	Traditional material	Plastic material	Advantage of plastic material
pipes guttering,	metal	PVC	light, does not corrode
window frames	wood	PVC	does not require paint for protection
crockery	china	melamine	light, does not break
carpets	wool	nylon, polyester	better wear

❏ for some uses, natural materials have advantages over synthetic materials,

   e.g. wool is warmer than synthetic fibres, melamine is less attractive than china

❏ most plastics are not **biodegradable** ('bio' refers to living things and 'degradable' means able to rot away), i.e. they can be broken down by bacteria found in the soil, in rivers and the sea

❏ the low density and durability of plastics can cause environmental problems,

   e.g. unsightly litter

❏ Biopol is a recently developed biodegradable plastic

❏ some plastics burn or smoulder to give off toxic fumes, including carbon monoxide; the fumes are related to the elements present in the plastics,

   e.g.

Plastic	Elements	Fumes
any	C	carbon monoxide in limited air
PVC	C, H, Cl	carbon monoxide hydrogen chloride
polyurethane	C, H, N	carbon monoxide hydrogen cyanide

❏ **thermoplastics** soften on heating and can be reshaped over and over again,

   e.g. nylon , polythene

❏ **thermosetting plastics** harden on heating and do not melt on reheating,

   e.g. bakelite, formica

Plastic	Property	Use
bakelite	heat-resisitant, rigid, non-conductor of electricity	plugs, sockets
formica	rigid, heat-resistant	kitchen work-tops

Addition polymers

❑ plastics are made of very long chain molecules; the large molecule is called a **polymer**

❑ polymers are made by the joining together of small molecules; the small molecule is called a **monomer**

❑ polymers made from unsaturated monomer units by the opening of carbon to carbon double bonds are called **addition polymers**; the process is called **addition polymersation**

❑ the name of the polymer is derived from the name of the monomer

Monomer	Polymer
ethene	poly(ethene)
propene	poly(propene)
styrene	polystyrene
vinyl chloride	polyvinylchloride (PVC)

❑ when thinking about addition polymerisation, it is useful to draw the alkene monomer in the shape of an ⊢⊣ with the double bond in the middle,

e.g.

$$\begin{array}{cc} H & H \\ | & | \\ C & = C \\ | & | \\ H & H \end{array} \quad \text{for ethene, } CH_2{=}CH_2$$

$$\begin{array}{cc} CH_3 & H \\ | & | \\ C & = C \\ | & | \\ H & H \end{array} \quad \text{for propene, } CH_3\text{-}CH{=}CH_2$$

❑ molecules of ethene (a monomer) can join together by the breaking of the carbon to carbon double bonds to form poly(ethene) (a polymer)

$$\begin{array}{cc} H & H \\ | & | \\ C{=}C \\ | & | \\ H & H \end{array} + \begin{array}{cc} H & H \\ | & | \\ C{=}C \\ | & | \\ H & H \end{array} + \begin{array}{cc} H & H \\ | & | \\ C{=}C \\ | & | \\ H & H \end{array} \rightarrow \begin{array}{cccccc} H & H & H & H & H & H \\ | & | & | & | & | & | \\ {-}C{-}C{-}C{-}C{-}C{-}C{-} \\ | & | & | & | & | & | \\ H & H & H & H & H & H \end{array}$$

❑ the polymerisation of ethene can be represented as:

$$n \begin{array}{cc} H & H \\ | & | \\ C{=}C \\ | & | \\ H & H \end{array} \rightarrow \left(\begin{array}{cc} H & H \\ | & | \\ {-}C{-}C{-} \\ | & | \\ H & H \end{array} \right)_n$$

where n is a large number

❑
$$-\overset{\displaystyle H}{\underset{\displaystyle H}{C}}-\overset{\displaystyle H}{\underset{\displaystyle H}{C}}-$$
is called the repeating unit

❑ other polymers can be formed in a similar way,
e.g.

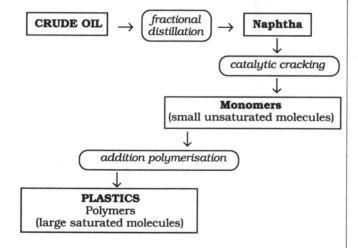

vinyl chloride   **polyvinylchloride**

❑ the processes involved in the production of plastics from crude oil are shown in the following flow diagram

CRUDE OIL → *fractional distillation* → **Naphtha**

↓

catalytic cracking

↓

Monomers
(small unsaturated molecules)

↓

addition polymerisation

↓

PLASTICS
Polymers
(large saturated molecules)

Condensation polymerisation

❑ **condensation polymers** are made from monomers with two functional groups in each molecule; the long chain is built up since condensation can occur at both ends of the molecule

❑ in **condensation polymerisation** the monomers usually link together by the loss of the elements to make water; a hydrogen atom from one monomer combines with a hydroxyl group from another,

   e.g.

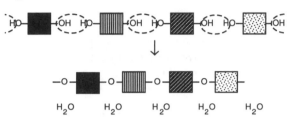

Polyesters

❑ **polyesters** are long chain molecules with many ester linkages

$$-\overset{O}{\underset{\|}{C}}-\blacksquare-\overset{O}{\underset{\|}{C}}-o-\square-o-\overset{O}{\underset{\|}{C}}-\blacksquare-\overset{O}{\underset{\|}{C}}-o-\square-o-\overset{O}{\underset{\|}{C}}-\blacksquare-\overset{O}{\underset{\|}{C}}-o-\square-o-$$

   —■—   and   —□—   represent different arrangements of carbon and hydrogen atoms

❑ polyesters are formed from alcohols with two -OH groups, one at either end of the molecules and acids with two

   $-\overset{O}{\underset{\|}{C}}-OH$

   groups, one at either end of the molecules; this means the polyester molecules can continue to grow in both directions

   HO—□—OH   HO—$\overset{O}{\underset{\|}{C}}$—■—$\overset{O}{\underset{\|}{C}}$—OH

   alcohol   **acid**

❑ the acid and the alcohol group can join together with the loss of the elements to form water

   HO—$\overset{O}{\underset{\|}{C}}$—■—$\overset{O}{\underset{\|}{C}}$—OH HO—□—OH HO—$\overset{O}{\underset{\|}{C}}$—■—$\overset{O}{\underset{\|}{C}}$—OH HO—□—OH

   ↓ **condensation polymerisation**

   $$-\overset{O}{\underset{\|}{C}}-\blacksquare-\overset{O}{\underset{\|}{C}}-o-\square-o-\overset{O}{\underset{\|}{C}}-\blacksquare-\overset{O}{\underset{\|}{C}}-o-\square-o-$$

Amines

❑ the **amines** are a homologous series of carbon compounds all containing nitrogen atoms

❑ the functional group in amines is the **amine** (or **amino**) group ($-NH_2$)

❑ each member of the series has a name which ends in -**amine** and a prefix which indicates the number of carbon atoms in the molecule.

e.g.

1 methylamine
H ‖ H-C-NH$_2$ ‖ H
CH_3NH_2 CH_5N

KEY
Number of carbon atoms
Name
Full structural formula
Shortened structural formula
Molecular formula

2 ethylamine
H H ‖ ‖ H-C—C-NH$_2$ ‖ ‖ H H
$CH_3-CH_2NH_2$ C_2H_7N

3 propylamine
H H H ‖ ‖ ‖ H-C—C—C-NH$_2$ ‖ ‖ ‖ H H H
$CH_3-CH_2-CH_2NH_2$ C_3H_9N

Polyamides

❑ **polyamides** are formed from molecules with amine groups and carboxylic acid groups

amine group   carboxylic acid group

❑ the acidic and the amino groups can join together with the loss of the elements to form water

↓   **condensation polymerisation**

☐ the $-\overset{\overset{\displaystyle O}{\|}}{C}-\overset{\overset{\displaystyle H}{|}}{N}-$ link is called an **amide** link and the polymer is called a polyamide

☐ nylon is a polyamide that can be made from two different monomer units; one is a diacid and the other is a diamine

diacid   **diamine**

↓   **condensation polymerisation**

☐ in practice, nylon is made from the chloride of the acid rather than the acid

☐ the condensation involves the elimination of hydrogen chloride molecules

diacid chloride   **diamine**

↓   **condensation polymerisation**

5. NATURAL PRODUCTS

Carbohydrates

❑ **carbohydrates** form an important class of food made by plants

❑ carbohydrates are needed to supply the body with energy

❑ carbohydrates are compounds which contain carbon, hydrogen and oxygen with the hydrogen and oxygen in the ratio of two to one,

e.g. fructose, $C_6H_{12}O_6$, is a carbohydrate but
ethylene glycol, $C_3H_8O_3$, is not

❑ carbohydrates can be divided into **starches** and **sugars**

e.g. glucose, fructose, maltose and sucrose (table sugar)

❑ **iodine solution** can be used to test for starch; a blue/black colour indicates a positive result

❑ **Benedict's solution** can be used to test for sugars; a yellow/orange/red/brown colour when the substance is heated in a test tube with Benedict's solution by a water bath indicates a positive result

❑ sucrose is an exception; it is a sugar which does **not** give a positive result when tested with Benedict's solution

Structure of carbohydrates

❑ sugars are carbohydrates with small molecules which can dissolve in water

❑ starch is a natural polymer made by the linking together of many glucose molecules (monomers)

❑ since the glucose molecules join together with the loss of the elements to make water, starch is a **condensation polymer**

plants convert the glucose into starch for storing energy

❏ during digestion starch is broken down to glucose which is carried by the blood stream to body cells

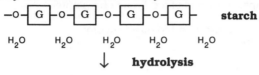

starch

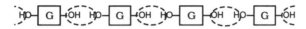

↓ hydrolysis

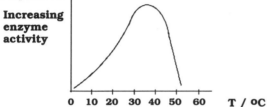

❏ since the breakdown of glucose involves the addition of the elements of water, this is an example of a **hydrolysis** reaction

❏ starch can be hydrolysed by acid and by enzymes

See
UNIT 2 PPA 3

❏ the efficiency of enzymes are affected by changes in temperature

Increasing enzyme activity

0 10 20 30 40 50 60   T / °C

❏ body enzymes function best at body temperature (37°C) and are destroyed at higher temperatures

Proteins

- [ ] proteins form an important class of food made by plants

- [ ] animals need proteins as part of a balanced diet for body-building and repair

- [ ] proteins are taken in by animals when plants or other animals are eaten

- [ ] proteins are the major structural materials of animal tissue,

  e.g. in hair, skin and nails

- [ ] proteins are involved in many human biological processes,

  e.g. enzymes, hormones (insulin) and haemoglobin

Structure of proteins

- [ ] plants and animals need a supply of **nitrogen** to build proteins

- [ ] proteins are natural polymers made by the linking together of many amino acid molecules (monomers)

- [ ] the structure of an amino acid molecule can be represented:

acid group   **amine (or amino) group**

- [ ] the ▢ represents the other arrangements of atoms in the various amino acids,

  e.g.

  glycine   **alanine**

- [ ] the acidic group and the amino group of different amino acid molecules can join together with the loss of the elements to form water

  condensation ↓

- since two reactants join up with the elimination of the elements to form water, the making of a protein is an example of **condensation polymerisation**

- the 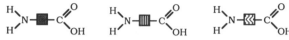 group is called a **peptide** link

- in the reverse process, protein molecules are broken down with the addition of the elements from water

hydrolysis ↓

- since the breakdown of the protein occurs due to the addition of the elements from water, this is an example of a **hydrolysis** reaction

- protein molecules have a very high molecular mass since the molecules consist of long chains often with several thousand amino acid molecules joined together

part of a 'protein' polymer

- there are over 20 different amino acids found in proteins; the different possible sequences of these amino acids allow for the wide variety of different protein molecules

- during digestion, insoluble protein in food is hydrolysed into amino acids; these smaller molecules can be absorbed into the bloodstream and taken to the various parts of the body to be reassembled in a different order to give the proteins that the body needs

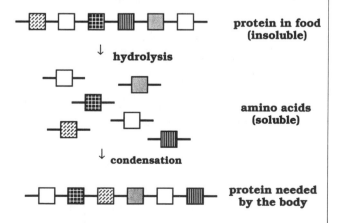

protein in food (insoluble)

↓ **hydrolysis**

amino acids (soluble)

↓ **condensation**

protein needed by the body

Fats and oils

❑ the prime function of fats and oils in the diet is to provide energy

❑ fats and oils are a more concentrated energy source than carbohydrates

❑ a rough comparison could be made by burning different foods below a boiling tube containing water and recording the temperature rises

❑ fats and oils can be classified according to their origin

Animal	Vegetable	Marine
pork fat	sunflower oil	cod liver oil
beef fat	rape seed oil	whale oil
	palm oil	
	olive oil	

❑ fats and oils are mixtures of molecules some of which are saturated and some of which are unsaturated

❑ there are differences between fats and oils

Fats	solid	more saturated molecules
Oils	liquid	more unsaturated molecules

❑ the lower melting points of oils compared with fats are related to the higher proportion of unsaturated molecules in oils

❑ the saturated molecules are more closely packed; as a result, the forces of attraction between the molecules is relatively strong and so fats have relatively high melting points

❑ the shape of the unsaturated molecules in oils does not allow for close packing of the molecules; consequently the forces of attraction between the molecules are weaker and hence the melting points of oils are lower than that of fats

❑ oils can be **hardened** to make them more suitable for use as margarine; partial removal of the unsaturation by the addition of hydrogen (hydrogenation), using a suitable catalyst, raises the melting point

Structure of fats and oils

❏ fats and oils are examples of esters

❏ fats and oils can be broken up to produce different carboxylic acids known as **fatty acids** and the one alkanol

❏ in fats and oils, fatty acids are always combined with propane-1,2,3-triol, commonly called **glycerol**

$$CH_2-OH$$
$$|$$
$$CH\ -OH$$
$$|$$
$$CH_2-OH$$

❏ the three fatty acid molecules combined with each molecule of glycerol may or may not be identical

$$CH_2-O-\overset{\overset{O}{\|}}{C}-R$$
$$|\qquad\overset{O}{\|}$$
$$CH\ -O-\overset{}{C}-R^*$$
$$|\qquad\overset{O}{\|}$$
$$CH_2-O-\overset{}{C}-R^{**}$$

R, R*, R**, may or may not be the same carbon chain

❏ hydrolysis of fats and oils produces glycerol and the fatty acid(s)

$$CH_2-O-\overset{\overset{O}{\|}}{C}-R$$
$$|\qquad\overset{O}{\|}$$
$$CH\ -O-\overset{}{C}-R^*$$
$$|\qquad\overset{O}{\|}$$
$$CH_2-O-\overset{}{C}-R^{**}$$

hydrolysis
$$\rightleftharpoons$$

$$CH_2-OH$$
$$|$$
$$CH\ -OH$$
$$|$$
$$CH_2-OH$$

glycerol

+

$$HO-\overset{\overset{O}{\|}}{C}-R$$

$$HO-\overset{\overset{O}{\|}}{C}-R^*$$

$$HO-\overset{\overset{O}{\|}}{C}-R^{**}$$

fatty acid(s)

Unit 3   Acids, Bases and Metals

1. ACIDS AND BASES

The pH scale

❑ the pH scale is a continuous range of numbers from below 0 to above 14 which indicate the acidity or alkalanity of solutions

❑ the pH number of a solution can be determined by colour matching using Universal indicator or pH paper (or a pH meter)

| DARK RED | ORANGE/YELLOW | GREEN | GREEN / BLUE | DARK BLUE |

| pH | 1 | 2 | 3 | 4 | 5 | 6 | 7 | 8 | 9 | 10 | 11 | 12 | 13 | 14 |

ACID   **NEUTRAL**   **ALKALI**

❑ acidic solutions have a pH less than 7

❑ alkalis have a pH greater than 7

❑ neutral solutions have a pH equal to 7

❑ pure water also has a pH equal to 7

Acids and alkalis

❑ acids and alkalis are in common use in both the laboratory and at home

	acids	**alkalis**
found in the home	as vinegar in fruit (citric acid)	in toothpaste in indigestion powder in oven cleaner in window cleaner
from oxide	sulphuric acid $H_2SO_{4(aq)}$ nitric acid $HNO_{3(aq)}$ carbonic acid $H_2CO_{3(aq)}$	sodium hydroxide $NaOH_{(aq)}$ potassium hydroxide $KOH_{(aq)}$ calcium hydroxide $Ca(OH)_{2(aq)}$
not from oxide	hydrochloric acid $HCl_{(aq)}$	ammonia $NH_{3(aq)}$

❑ non-metal oxides which dissolve in water produce acidic solutions,

e.g. *sulphur dioxide, nitrogen dioxide, carbon dioxide*

❑ hydrogen oxide (water) has a pH equal to 7

❑ metal oxides and hydroxides which dissolve in water produce alkaline solutions,

e.g. *sodium oxide, sodium hydroxide*

❑ metal oxides and hydroxides which are insoluble in water do **not** affect the pH of water,

e.g. *copper(II) oxide, iron(II) hydroxide*

❑ the solubilities of selected metal oxides and hydroxides are shown on page 5 of the Data Booklet

❑ ammonia gas, $NH_3(g)$, dissolves in water to produce an alkali; the alkali is called ammonia solution, $NH_3(aq)$

❑ solid sodium hydroxide and hydrogen chloride gas do **not** affect dry pH paper

❑ water must be present to produce $OH^-(aq)$ ions (alkali) and $H^+(aq)$ ions (acid)

$$Na^+OH^-(s) \quad \rightarrow \quad Na^+(aq) \text{ and } OH^-(aq)$$
sodium hydroxide solution

$$HCl(g) \quad \rightarrow \quad H^+(aq) \text{ and } Cl^-(aq)$$
hydrochloric acid

Hydrogen, $H^+(aq)$, and hydroxide, $OH^-(aq)$, ions

❑ all solutions in water contain both $H^+(aq)$ ions and $OH^-(aq)$ ions; it is the relative concentrations of these ions which decides whether a solution is acid, alkali or neutral

❑ in acids, the concentration of $H^+(aq)$ ions is greater than the concentration of $OH^-(aq)$ ions

❑ when an acid is diluted, the solution becomes less acid; the pH increases because the concentration of $H^+(aq)$ ions decreases

❑ in alkalis, the concentration of $OH^-(aq)$ ions is greater than the concentration of $H^+(aq)$ ions

❑ when an alkali is diluted, the solution becomes less alkaline; the pH decreases because the concentration of $OH^-(aq)$ decreases

❏ in water (and neutral solutions) there is a small number of H^+(aq) and OH^-(aq) ions; this is because a small number of water molecules split up

$$H_2O(l) \quad \rightarrow \quad H^+(aq) \quad + \quad OH^-(aq)$$

many water molecules   **very few ions**

❏ since each water molecule can form one H^+(aq) ion and one OH^-(aq) ion, the concentration of H^+(aq) ions in pure water (and neutral solutions) is equal to the concentration of OH^-(aq) ions

❏ the splitting up of water molecules is a **reversible** reaction, i.e. at the same time as water molecules are splitting up, H^+(aq) and OH^-(aq) ions are reforming water molecules

$$H_2O(l) \quad \rightleftharpoons \quad H^+(aq) \quad + \quad OH^-(aq)$$

❏ the rate at which water molecules dissociate or ionise (split up) is equal to the rate at which H^+(aq) ions and OH^-(aq) ions react to form water molecules; hence the concentrations of H^+(aq) ions and OH^-(aq) ions do not change even although the forward and the reverse reactions continue

❏ when the concentrations of reactants and products remain constant, the reversible reaction is said to be at **equilibrium**

❏ when a reaction is at equilibrium, the concentrations of reactants and products are not necessarily equal

❏ since water is only a poor conductor of electricity, there must be as many more ions than molecules.

Concentration

❏ the concentration of an aqueous solution is the mass of solute dissolved in a certain volume of water

❏ this can be expressed as grams per litre, $g\,l^{-1}$

❏ in chemistry, the concentration is normally expressed in terms of the number of moles of the solute in one litre of water, i.e. $mol\,l^{-1}$

❏ a solution labelled $1\,mol\,l^{-1}$ contains one mole of solute in one litre of solution

❏ a solution labelled $2\,mol\,l^{-1}$ contains two moles of solute in one litre of solution

Example 1

How many moles are there in 100 cm^3 of sodium hydroxide solution, concentration 0.4 $mol\,l^{-1}$?

$0.4\,mol\,l^{-1}$ is 0.4 mol in 1 litre

1000 cm^3 ⟷ 0.4 mol

100 cm^3 ⟷ **0.04 mol**

Example 2

What is the concentration of a solution of hydrochloric acid containing 0.1 mol in 50 cm^3?

50 cm^3 ⟷ 0.1 mol

1000 cm^3 ⟷ 2 mol

i.e. the concentration is **2 $mol\,l^{-1}$**.

Example 3

What volume of a sodium carbonate solution, concentration 2 $mol\,l^{-1}$, contains 0.5 mol?

$2\,mol\,l^{-1}$ is 2 mol in 1 litre

2 mol ⟷ 1000 cm^3

0.5 mol ⟷ **250 cm^3**

Example 4

How many grams of hydrogen chloride are required to make 200 cm^3 of hydrochloric acid, concentration 2 mol l^{-1}?

Step 1 Calculate the number of moles required.

2 mol l^{-1} is 2 mol in 1 litre

1000 cm^3 ←——→ 2 mol

200 cm^3 ←——→ <u>0.4 mol</u>

Step 2 Calculate the mass of one mole of hydrogen chloride.

formula   HCl

relative atomic masses 1 + 35.5

one mole   <u>36.5 g</u>

Step 3 Calculate the mass of hydrogen chloride needed.

1 mol of hydrogen chloride has a mass of 36.5 g

1 mol   ←——→ 36.5 g

0.4 mol   ←——→ **14.6 g**

i.e. **14.6 g** of hydrogen chloride are required to make 200 cm^3 of hydrochloric acid, concentration 2 mol l^{-1}.

Example 5

What is the concentration of a solution which contains 5.85 g of sodium chloride in 500 cm^3 of solution?

Step 1 Calculate the mass of one mole of sodium chloride.

formula   NaCl

relative atomic masses 23 + 35.5

one mole   <u>58.5 g</u>

Step 2 Calculate the number of moles of sodium chloride present in the solution.

58.5 g   ←——→ 1 mol

5.85 g   ←——→ <u>0.1 mol</u>

Step 3 Calculate the concentration of the solution.

500 cm^3 ←——→ 0.1 mol

1000 cm^3 ←——→ **0.2 mol**

i.e. the concentration of the sodium chloride solution is **0.2 mol l^{-1}**.

Strong and weak acids

❑ a **strong acid** is one in which all the molecules are dissociated (ionised) when dissolved in water,

    e.g. hydrochloric acid

$$HCl(g) \quad + \quad (aq) \quad \rightarrow \quad H^+(aq) \quad + \quad Cl^-(aq)$$

    molecules   **ions**
    hydrogen chloride gas   **hydrochloric acid**

❑ a solution of hydrogen chloride gas will exist entirely as hydrogen and chloride ions; there will be no hydrogen chloride molecules present

❑ other strong acids include sulphuric and nitric acids

❑ a strong acid can be either concentrated or dilute depending on the number of moles of acid per litre of solution; the same applies to a weak acid

❑ a **weak acid** is one in which only some of the molecules are dissociated (ionised) when dissolved in water,

    e.g. ethanoic acid

$$CH_3COOH(aq) \quad \rightleftharpoons \quad CH_3COO^-(aq) \quad + \quad H^+(aq)$$

    molecules   **ions**

❑ in solutions of carboxylic acids, an equilibrium is set up between the ethanoic acid molecules and the hydrogen and ethanoate ions

❑ since the equilibrium position lies to the left, an ethanoic acid solution will exist mainly as molecules

❑ when comparing properties of strong and weak acids, solutions of equal concentration (equimolar) should be used

Measurement	Hydrochloric acid	Ethanoic acid
pH	higher (further from 7) →	
Conductivity	← higher	
Rate of reaction with magnesium	← faster	

❑ the pH is lower, the conductivity is higher and the rate of reaction with magnesium is faster with hydrochloric acid solution due to the reduced concentration of hydrogen ions, $H^+(aq)$, which results from the equilibrium in ethanoic acid

Strong and weak bases

❑ a **strong base** is one in which all the available hydroxide ions are released in solution,

e.g. *sodium hydroxide*

$$Na^+OH^-_{(s)} \quad + \quad H_2O_{(l)} \quad \rightarrow \quad Na^+_{(aq)} \quad + \quad OH^-_{(aq)}$$

sodium hydroxide   sodium hydroxide
solid   solution

❑ a **weak base** is made up of molecules;
only some of the molecules are dissociated (ionised) when dissolved in water,

e.g. *ammonia*

$$NH_{3(aq)} \quad + \quad H_2O_{(l)} \quad \rightleftharpoons \quad NH_4^+_{(aq)} \quad + \quad OH^-_{(aq)}$$

molecules   ions

❑ in ammonia solution, there is an equilibrium between the ammonium and hydroxide ions and the ammonia and water molecules

❑ since the equilibrium position lies to the left, a solution of ammonia will exist mainly as molecules

❑ when comparing properties of strong and weak bases, solutions of equal concentration (equimolar) should be used

Measurement	Sodium hydroxide solution	Ammonia solution
pH	⬅ higher (further from 7)	
Conductivity	⬅ higher	

❑ the pH and conductivity are lower for the ammonia solution due to the lower concentrations of ions which result from the equilibrium

2. SALT PREPARATION

Bases

❑ a **base** is a substance which neutralises acids,

  e.g. metal hydroxide, metal oxide, metal carbonate, ammonia

❑ **alkalis** are solutions which are a subset of the set of bases, i.e. formed from those bases which dissolve in water, producing hydroxide ions

compounds which neutralise acids,	formed when a base dissolves in water,
e.g. copper oxide,	*e.g.*
copper hydroxide, sodium oxide, sodium hydroxide	*sodium hydroxide solution*

❑ sodium oxide and sodium hydroxide are both bases which dissolve in water to form sodium hydroxide solution (an alkali)

$$Na_2O(s) \quad + \quad H_2O(l) \quad \rightarrow \quad 2NaOH(aq)$$

$$NaOH(s) \quad + \quad H_2O(l) \quad \rightarrow \quad NaOH(aq)$$

❑ copper oxide and copper hydroxide are insoluble in water; they are bases since they neutralise acids but they do not form alkalis

❑ when a base dissolves in water, the pH increases

Neutralisation

❑ **neutralisation** is a reaction of acids with bases

❑ neutralisation moves the pH of an acid or alkali towards 7

❑ in the reaction of an acid with an alkali, the H^+(aq) ions react with OH^-(aq) ions

$$H^+(aq) \quad + \quad OH^-(aq) \quad \rightarrow \quad H_2O(l)$$

❑ in the reaction of an acid with a metal oxide, the H^+(aq) ions react with oxide ions

$$2H^+(aq) \quad + \quad O^{2-}(s) \quad \rightarrow \quad H_2O(l)$$

❑ in the reaction of an acid with a metal carbonate, the H^+(aq) ions react with carbonate ions; carbon dioxide is produced as well as water

$$2H^+(aq) + CO_3^{2-}(s) \rightarrow H_2O(l) + CO_2(g)$$

❑ many neutralisation reactions are important,

e.g. addition of lime to reduce soil or lake acidity,
treatment of acid indigestion,
reaction of ammonia with acid to produce fertilisers in
the chemical industry

Acids and metals

❑ metals also react with acid moving the pH towards 7,

e.g. zinc reacts with dilute sulphuric acid

❑ in this reaction the H^+(aq) ions gain electrons to form molecules of hydrogen gas; water is **not** formed

$$2H^+(aq) + 2e^- \rightarrow H_2(g)$$

❑ the test for hydrogen is that it burns with a 'pop'

Acid rain

❑ sulphur dioxide, produced by the burning of fossil fuels, dissolves in water in the atmosphere to produce acid rain

❑ nitrogen dioxide, produced by the sparking of air in car engines, also dissolves in rain-water, contributing to acid rain

❑ a lot of damage to the environment is caused by acid rain,

e.g. buildings - carbonates in some stone and some mortar
dissolve in acid,
metal structures - steel and several other metals are
dissolved by acid,
plants - most cannot grow in very acidic soils,
fish - cannot live in acidic loch or river water

Volumetric titrations

❏ the volume of acid (from a burette) required to neutralise a fixed volume of alkali (from a pipette) can be found using a suitable indicator to determine the end-point of the reaction

❏ if the concentration of the acid or the alkali is known then the concentration of the other can be calculated using the balanced equation

❏ in a neutralisation reaction, neutralisation is complete when all the H^+(aq) ions from the acid have been removed by exactly the same number of OH^-(aq) ions to form water,

i.e. number of moles $\quad=\quad$ number of moles
of H^+(aq) $\qquad\qquad$ of OH^-(aq)

$\quad$ volume in litres $\qquad\qquad$ volume in litres
$\qquad$ x $\qquad\qquad\qquad\qquad$ x
$\quad$ conc. $\qquad=\qquad$ conc.
$\qquad$ x $\qquad\qquad\qquad\qquad$ x
$\quad$ number of H^+(aq) $\qquad$ number of OH^-(aq)

OR $\quad$ multiplying both sides by 1000

$\quad$ volume in cm^3 $\qquad\qquad$ volume in cm^3
$\qquad$ x $\qquad\qquad\qquad\qquad$ x
$\quad$ conc. $\qquad=\qquad$ conc.
$\qquad$ x $\qquad\qquad\qquad\qquad$ x
$\quad$ number of H^+(aq) $\qquad$ number of OH^-(aq)

Example 1

What volume of NaOH(aq) (concentration 2 mol l⁻¹) is required to neutralise 50 cm^3 of HNO_3(aq) (concentration 1 mol l⁻¹)?

number of moles of H^+(aq) $\quad=\quad$ number of moles of OH^-(aq)

$\quad$ volume in litres $\qquad\qquad$ volume in litres
$\qquad$ x $\qquad\qquad\qquad\qquad$ x
$\quad$ conc. $\qquad=\qquad$ conc.
$\qquad$ x $\qquad\qquad\qquad\qquad$ x
$\quad$ number of H^+(aq) $\qquad$ number of OH^-(aq)

$$50 \ x \ 1 \ x \ 1 \ = \ V \ x \ 2 \ x \ 1$$

$$V \ = \ \frac{50 \ cm^3}{2}$$

$$= \ \mathbf{25 \ cm^3}$$

Example 2

If 25 cm^3 of H_2SO_4(aq) is required to neutralise 25 cm^3 of KOH(aq) (concentration 0.1 mol l^{-1}), what is the concentration of the H_2SO_4(aq)?

number of moles of H$^+$(aq) = number of moles of OH$^-$(aq)

25 x conc. x 2 = 25 x 0.1 x 1

conc = $\dfrac{25 \times 0.1}{50}$ mol l^{-1}

= **0.05 mol l^{-1}**

Naming salts

❑ salts are substances in which the hydrogen ions of an acid have been replaced by metal ions (or ammonium ions),

    e.g. sodium chloride,
       potassium nitrate,
       ammonium sulphate

❑ salts are formed by the reactions of acids with bases or metals

❑ the first part of the name of a salt is the name of the metal (or the name ammonium)

❑ the second part of the name of a salt comes from the name of the acid

Acid		Salt
hydrochloric	- - - - -	chloride
sulphuric	- - - - -	sulphate
nitric	- - - - -	nitrate

❑ **ALKALI + ACID → SALT + WATER**

e.g.
sodium hydroxide + nitric acid → sodium nitrate + water

$$NaOH(aq) + HNO_3(aq) → NaNO_3(aq) + H_2O(l)$$

❑ an indicator has to be used to find the volume of alkali required to neutralise a known volume of acid

❑ the experiment is repeated using the same volumes without the indicator

❑ the solution (filtrate) is evaporated to dryness to obtain a solid sample of the salt

❑ **METAL OXIDE + ACID → SALT + WATER**

e.g.
zinc oxide + hydrochloric acid → zinc chloride + water

$$ZnO(s) + 2HCl(aq) → ZnCl_2(aq) + H_2O(l)$$

❑ an insoluble metal oxide is used

❑ the metal oxide will react with the acid but will **not** dissolve in the neutral solution

❑ excess metal oxide is added to the acid

❑ the unreacted metal oxide can be removed by filtering

❑ the solution (filtrate) is evaporated to dryness to obtain a solid sample of the salt

❑ **METAL CARBONATE + ACID →**
SALT + WATER + CARBON DIOXIDE

See UNIT 3 PPA 1

e.g.
calcium carbonate + nitric acid →
calcium nitrate + water + carbon dioxide

$$CaCO_3(s) + 2HNO_3(aq) → Ca(NO_3)_2(aq) + H_2O(l) + CO_2(g)$$

❑ the method is the same as for an insoluble metal oxide

❑ when all the acid has been neutralise,d the gas is no longer produced

❑ **METAL + ACID → SALT + HYDROGEN**

e.g.

zinc + sulphuric acid → zinc sulphate + hydrogen

$Zn(s) + H_2SO_4(aq) → ZnSO_4(aq) + H_2(g)$

❑ the method is the same as for an insoluble metal oxide

❑ when preparing a salt it is preferable to react an acid with an insoluble base (or metal); when all the acid has been neutralised the excess solid remains and can be removed by filtering

Nitrogen salts

❑ some nitrogen salts are made by neutralisation reactions for use as fertilisers,

e.g. potassium nitrate

potassium hydroxide + nitric acid →
$\qquad$ potassium nitrate + water

$KOH(aq) + HNO_3(aq) → KNO_3(aq) + H_2O(l)$

e.g. ammonium nitrate

ammonia + nitric acid → ammonium nitrate

$NH_3(g) + HNO_3(aq) → NH_4NO_3(aq)$

❑ since these salts are soluble in water, the nitrogen for plant growth is able to be taken in by the roots of plants in solution

Precipitation

❑ **precipitation** is the reaction of two solutions to form an insoluble product,

e.g.

barium chloride solution + sodium sulphate solution
$\qquad$ → barium sulphate solid + sodium chloride solution

$BaCl_2(aq) + Na_2SO_4(aq) → BaSO_4(s) + 2NaCl(aq)$

❑ the insoluble product is called a **precipitate**,

e.g. $BaSO_4(s)$

❑ the insoluble product can be removed from the solution by filtration

❑ a list of insoluble compounds which can be prepared by precipitation can be found on page 5 of the Data Booklet

❑ insoluble salts can be prepared by precipitation,

e.g. silver nitrate, barium sulphate

Ionic equations

❑ **spectator ions** are ions which do not take part in a chemical reaction

❑ ionic equations show only the ions which are involved in the reactions, i.e. the spectator ions are omitted

Example 1

Reaction of a dilute acid with an alkali

e.g. the reaction of sodium hydroxide solution with dilute hydrochloric acid

$$NaOH(aq) + HCl(aq) \rightarrow NaCl(aq) + H_2O(l)$$

❑ this equation can be rewritten to show the ions present; since water is made up almost entirely of molecules (covalent) it is left unchanged

$$Na^+(aq) \text{ and } OH^-(aq) + H^+(aq) \text{ and } Cl^-(aq)$$
$$\rightarrow Na^+(aq) \text{ and } Cl^-(aq) + H_2O(l)$$

❑ both the $Na^+(aq)$ and $Cl^-(aq)$ have not changed during the reaction; they are both spectator ions and can be cancelled out to show the actual reaction taking place

$$\cancel{Na^+(aq)} \text{ and } OH^-(aq) + H^+(aq) \text{ and } \cancel{Cl^-(aq)}$$
$$\rightarrow \cancel{Na^+(aq)} \text{ and } \cancel{Cl^-(aq)} + H_2O(l)$$

hence $OH^-(aq) + H^+(aq) \rightarrow H_2O(l)$

❑ this equation shows the $OH^-(aq)$ of the alkali reacting with the $H^+(aq)$ of the acid; this reaction takes place during the **neutralisation** of **any** acid with **any** alkali

Example 2

Reaction of a dilute acid with a metal cabonate

e.g. the reaction of dilute sulphuric acid with sodium carbonate solution

$$H_2SO_4(aq) + Na_2CO_3(aq) \rightarrow$$
$$Na_2SO_4(aq) + H_2O(l) + CO_2(g)$$

❑ both water and carbon dioxide are made up of molecules

❑ rewriting to show the ions present gives:

$$2H^+(aq) \text{ and } SO_4^{2-}(aq) + 2Na^+(aq) \text{ and } CO_3^{2-}(aq)$$
$$\rightarrow 2Na^+(aq) \text{ and } SO_4^{2-}(aq) + H_2O(l) + CO_2(g)$$

- both the Na^+(aq) and the SO_4^{2-}(aq) are spectator ions and can be cancelled out

$2H^+$(aq) and ~~SO_4^{2-}~~(aq) + ~~$2Na^+$~~(aq) and CO_3^{2-}(aq)

→ ~~$2Na^+$~~(aq) and ~~SO_4^{2-}~~(aq) + H_2O(l) + CO_2(g)

- the ion equation shows what actually happens in any reaction of a dilute acid with a solution of a metal carbonate

$2H^+$(aq) + CO_3^{2-}(aq) → H_2O(l) + CO_2(g)

Example 3

Reaction of a dilute acid with a metal oxide

e.g. the reaction of copper(II) oxide with dilute hydrochloric acid

CuO(s) + $2HCl$(aq) → $CuCl_2$(aq) + H_2O(l)

- this equation can be rewritten to show the ions present

$Cu^{2+}O^{2-}$(s) + $2H^+$(aq) and $2Cl^-$(aq)

→ Cu^{2+}(aq) and $2Cl^-$(aq) + H_2O(l)

- both the copper ion and the chloride ion are spectator ions and can be cancelled out

~~Cu^{2+}~~O^{2-}(s) + $2H^+$(aq) and ~~$2Cl^-$~~(aq)

→ ~~Cu^{2+}~~(aq) and ~~$2Cl^-$~~(aq) + H_2O(l)

- this leaves an equation which shows what is actually happening during the reaction of a metal oxide with a dilute acid

O^{2-}(s) + $2H^+$(aq) → H_2O(l)

Example 4

A precipitation reaction

e.g. the reaction of sodium chloride solution with silver nitrate solution produces a precipitate of silver chloride

$NaCl$(aq) + $AgNO_3$(aq) → $NaNO_3$(aq) + $AgCl$(s)

- in solution, the ions in an ionic compound are free to move whereas the ions in a solid are tightly packed together

Na^+(aq) and Cl^-(aq) + Ag^+(aq) and NO_3^-(aq)

→ Na^+(aq) and NO_3^-(aq) + Ag^+Cl^-(s)

❏ the spectator ions are the $Na^+(aq)$ and $NO_3^-(aq)$ and these ions can be cancelled out

$\cancel{Na^+}(aq)$ and $Cl^-(aq)$ + $Ag^+(aq)$ and $\cancel{NO_3}(aq)$

→ $\cancel{Na^+}(aq)$ and $\cancel{NO_3}(aq)$ + $Ag^+Cl^-(s)$

hence $Cl^-(aq)$ + $Ag^+(aq)$ → $Ag^+Cl^-(s)$

❏ in any precipitation reaction

$A^+X^-(aq)$ + $B^+Y^-(aq)$ → $A^+Y^-(s)$ + $B^+X^-(aq)$

❏ the spectator ions can be cancelled out to leave:

$A^+(aq)$ + $Y^-(aq)$ → $A^+Y^-(s)$

3.   METALS

Electricity

❑   electricity is a flow of charged particles,

e.g. *electrons through metal wires, ions through solutions of ionic compounds and molten ionic compounds*

❑   chemical reactions are used to generate electricity

❑   an arrangement which converts chemical energy to electrical energy is called a **cell**

❑   two or more cells joined together make a **battery**

❑   the two terms, cell and battery, are now interchangeable

❑   most batteries have to be replaced as the chemicals are used up in the reactions

The electrochemical series

❑   all metals tend to form ions in solution

❑   the electrons are left on the metal, giving the metal a negative charge

❑   all metals do not have the same ability to form ions

metal A   **metal B**

❑   metal **A** has a greater potential than metal **B** to form ions and leave electrons on the surface of the metal

❑   if metal **A** is connected to metal **B** as shown, electrons will flow from metal **A** to metal **B**

flow of electrons

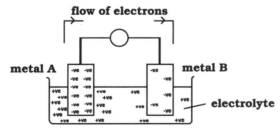

metal A   **metal B**

electrolyte

❑   the purpose of the electrolyte is to complete the circuit

❑   a voltmeter can measure the difference in potential of the metals to form ions

See
UNIT 3 PPA 2

- ❏ the potential difference is also known as the voltage

- ❏ the metals can be placed in an order which compares the energy involved in metal atoms forming ions in solution; this order is called the **electrochemical series**

- ❏ metals high up in the electrochemical series tend to lose electrons easily, i.e. prefer to exist as ions

- ❏ metals low down in the electrochemical series tend to hold on to their electrons, i.e. prefer to exist as atoms

- ❏ when two different metals (plus an electrolyte) are connected, electrons flow through the external circuit from the metal higher in the electrochemical series to the metal lower down,

e.g.

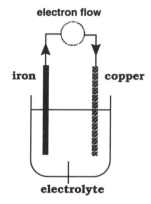

- ❏ different metal pairs produce different voltages

- ❏ metals which are far apart in the series produce higher voltages

- ❏ the position of some metals in the electrochemical series is shown on page 7 of the Data Booklet

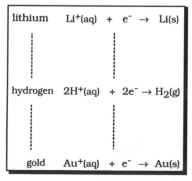

lithium $Li^+(aq) + e^- \rightarrow Li(s)$ good at supplying electrons

↑ metals above hydrogen react with dilute acids

hydrogen $2H^+(aq) + 2e^- \rightarrow H_2(g)$ hydrogen is included because of the reactions of metals with dilute acids

↓ metals below hydrogen do **not** react with dilute acids

gold $Au^+(aq) + e^- \rightarrow Au(s)$ poor at supplying electrons

Displacement reactions

❑ a displacement reaction occurs when a metal higher up in the electrochemical series is added to a solution containing ions of a metal lower down in the series,

*e.g. zinc displaces copper from copper(II) sulphate solution but **not** magnesium from magnesium nitrate solution*

❑ the electrochemical series can be used to explain/predict observations

Zinc with copper(II) sulphate solution

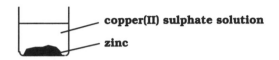

copper(II) sulphate solution

zinc

❑ zinc is higher than copper in the electrochemical series

❑ zinc atoms give electrons to copper ions

❑ zinc metal starts to 'disappear' as zinc atoms lose electrons to form zinc ions which dissolve into solution

$$Zn(s) \rightarrow Zn^{2+}(aq) + 2e^-$$

❑ copper ions in solution react to form copper atoms which appear as a solid

$$Cu^{2+}(aq) + 2e^- \rightarrow Cu(s)$$

❑ the solution eventually turns colourless as blue copper ions are used up

❑ the transfer of electrons can be shown using a cell

Cells

❑ electricity can be produced in a cell by connecting two different metals in solutions of their metal ions

(a) The magnesum/zinc cell

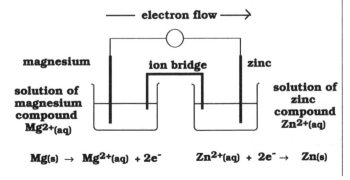

electron flow ⟶

magnesium   ion bridge   zinc

solution of magnesium compound $Mg^{2+}(aq)$ solution of zinc compound $Zn^{2+}(aq)$

$$Mg(s) \rightarrow Mg^{2+}(aq) + 2e^- \qquad Zn^{2+}(aq) + 2e^- \rightarrow Zn(s)$$

❑ electrons flow from the metal higher in the electrochemical series to the metal lower down

❑ magnesium atoms lose electrons to form magnesium ions which dissolve into the solution

$$Mg(s) \rightarrow Mg^{2+}(aq) + 2e^-$$

❑ the magnesium electrode decreases in mass

❑ zinc ions gain electrons to form zinc atoms which appear as a solid on the electrode

$$Zn^{2+}(aq) + 2e^- \rightarrow Zn(s)$$

❑ the zinc electrode increases in mass

❑ ions move in the ion bridge (salt bridge) to complete the circuit

(b) The iodide ion/iron(III) ion cell

❑ electricity can be produced in a cell in which at least one of the half-cells does not involve metal atoms

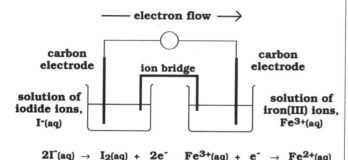

— electron flow ⟶

carbon electrode | ion bridge | carbon electrode

solution of iodide ions, $I^-(aq)$ | solution of iron(III) ions, $Fe^{3+}(aq)$

$$2I^-(aq) \rightarrow I_2(aq) + 2e^- \qquad Fe^{3+}(aq) + e^- \rightarrow Fe^{2+}(aq)$$

❑ electrons flow through the meter from the iodide ions to the iron(III) ions

❑ iodide ions lose electrons to form iodine molecules which dissolve into the solution

$$2I^-(aq) \rightarrow I_2(aq) + 2e^-$$

❑ iron(III) ions gain electrons to form iron(II) ions which dissolve in the solution

$$Fe^{3+}(aq) + e^- \rightarrow Fe^{2+}(aq)$$

❑ the presence of iron(III) ions can be shown using ferroxyl indicator (see page 97)

❑ ions move in the ion bridge (salt bridge) to complete the circuit

Oxidation and reduction

❑ **oxidation** is the loss of electrons by a reactant,

e.g. $Zn(s) \rightarrow Zn^{2+}(aq) + 2e^-$

❑ a metal element reacting to form a compound is an example of oxidation,

e.g. magnesium + oxygen → magnesium oxide

❑ **reduction** is the gain of electrons by a reactant,

e.g. $Cu^{2+}(aq) + 2e^- \rightarrow Cu(s)$

❑ a compound reacting to form a metal element is an example of reduction,

e.g. copper oxide + carbon monoxide →
copper + carbon dioxide

❑ oxidation cannot occur without reduction, and vice versa

❑ Oxidation is Loss : **OIL**

❑ Reduction is Gain : **RIG**

❑ oxidation cannot occur without reduction, and vice versa

❑ oxidation and reduction reactions can be written as ion-electron equations

❑ ion-electron equations for reduction reactions can be found on page 7 of the Data Booklet,

e.g. $Cu^{2+}(aq) + 2e^- \rightarrow Cu(s)$

❑ to obtain ion-electron equations for oxidation reactions, the equations in the Data Booklet must be turned round,

e.g. $Mg(s) \rightarrow Mg^{2+}(aq) + 2e^-$

❑ oxidation and reduction reactions need not involve metal atoms/metal ions,

e.g. $SO_3^{2-}(aq) + H_2O(l) \rightarrow SO_4^{2-}(aq) + 2H^+(aq) + 2e^-$
oxidation

$Br_2(aq) + 2e^- \rightarrow 2Br^-(aq)$
reduction

❑ in a test tube displacement reaction, atoms of the metal higher up in the electrochemical series are oxidised; the ions of the metal lower down in the series are reduced,

e.g. zinc/copper(II) sulphate solution

$Zn(s) \rightarrow Zn^{2+}(aq) + 2e^-$ oxidation
$Cu^{2+}(aq) + 2e^- \rightarrow Cu(s)$ reduction

❏ during electrolysis, oxidation occurs at the positive electrode and reduction occurs at the negative electrode,

e.g. electrolysis of copper(II) chloride solution

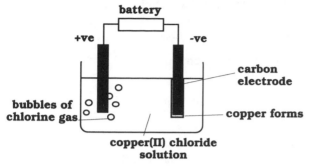

$$2Cl^-_{(aq)} \rightarrow Cl_{2(g)} + 2e^- \qquad Cu^{2+}_{(aq)} + 2e^- \rightarrow Cu_{(s)}$$

❏ copper ions are reduced at the negative electrode
$$Cu^{2+}_{(aq)} + 2e^- \rightarrow Cu_{(s)}$$

❏ chloride ions are oxidised at the positive electrode
$$2Cl^-_{(aq)} \rightarrow Cl_{2(g)} + 2e^-$$

Redox reactions

❏ redox reactions involve the transfer of electrons from one atom, molecule or ion to another

❏ to form the overall redox reaction, the ion-electron equations for the oxidation and reduction must be combined, ensuring that the number of electrons in the oxidation step cancels out with the number of electrons in the reduction step

Example 1

the reaction of magnesium with copper sulphate solution

oxidation $\qquad Mg_{(s)} \rightarrow Mg^{2+}_{(aq)} + 2e^-$

reduction $\qquad Cu^{2+}_{(aq)} + 2e^- \rightarrow Cu_{(s)}$

────────────────────────────────

redox reaction $Mg_{(s)} + Cu^{2+}_{(aq)} \rightarrow Mg^{2+}_{(aq)} + Cu_{(s)}$

Example 2

the reaction of aluminium with dilute hydrochloric acid

oxidation $Al(s)$ $\rightarrow$ $Al^{3+}(aq)$ + $3e^-$

reduction $2H^+(aq)$ + $2e^-$ $\rightarrow$ $H_2(g)$

To balance out the electrons, the oxidation must be multiplied by 2, and the reduction by 3.

$2Al(s)$ $\rightarrow$ $2Al^{3+}(aq)$ + $6e^-$

$6H^+(aq)$ + $6e^-$ $\rightarrow$ $3H_2(g)$

_____

$2Al(s)$ + $6H^+(aq)$ $\rightarrow$ $2Al^{3+}(aq)$ + $3H_2(g)$

Reactions of metals

❏ metals can be placed in order of their readiness to take part in chemical reactions; this is called the **reactivity series**

❏ reactive metals are at the top and unreactive (inactive) metals are at the bottom

❏ reactions with oxygen, water and dilute acid can be used to put the metals in order

❏ the order is based on observations,
e.g. speed of reactions, energy released

❏ the order is very similar to (but not identical to) the order in the electrochemical series

See
UNIT 3 PPA 3

	As elements: most reactive metals at top				As compounds: least reactive compounds at top
Metal	with oxygen	with water	with acid	with compounds	as oxides
potassium	metals which burn to form metal oxide (higher ones also burn in air at 15 °C) .... metals which form oxide on the surface only	metals which displace hydrogen from cold water; an alkaline solution is formed	metals too reactive to try in acid .... metals which displace hydrogen from acid .... metals which do not displace hydrogen from acids	in general each metal can displace any metal below it from one of its compounds	metal oxides do not decompose on heating with carbon or carbon monoxide; electrical energy required to decompose compounds metal oxides decompose on heating with carbon or carbon monoxide .... metal oxides decompose on heating to form metal
sodium					
lithium					
calcium					
magnesium					
aluminium					
zinc					
iron					
nickel					
tin					
lead					
hydrogen					
copper					
silver					
mercury					
gold					

❏ hydrogen is included because of the reactions of metals with dilute acids

Metals as resources

- an **ore** is a naturally occurring compound of a metal,

  e.g. iron ore contains iron oxide

- metals which are found **uncombined** are not joined up with other elements

- the less reactive metals are found uncombined,

  e.g. gold, silver

- since they are very unreactive and therefore found uncombined gold and silver have been known since earliest civilisation

- the more reactive metals have to be extracted (obtained) from their ores

- some metals can be obtained from metal oxides by heat alone,

  e.g. gold, silver

- some metals can only be obtained from metal oxides by heating with carbon or carbon monoxide,

  e.g. iron, lead

- the more reactive metals are obtained by electrolysis of molten ores,

  e.g. aluminium, magnesium

- as a result of the need for electricity, the large scale extraction of the more reactive metals only started in the last century

Production of iron from iron ore

❑ in industry the production of iron from iron ore is carried out in the Blast Furnace

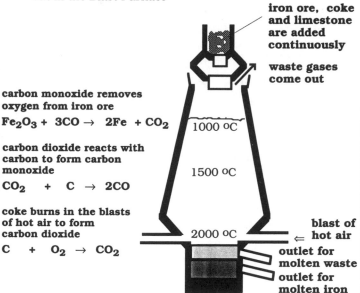

iron ore, coke and limestone are added continuously

waste gases come out

carbon monoxide removes oxygen from iron ore

$Fe_2O_3 + 3CO \rightarrow 2Fe + CO_2$

1000 ºC

carbon dioxide reacts with carbon to form carbon monoxide

$CO_2 + C \rightarrow 2CO$

1500 ºC

coke burns in the blasts of hot air to form carbon dioxide

$C + O_2 \rightarrow CO_2$

2000 ºC

blast of hot air

outlet for molten waste

outlet for molten iron

Corrosion

❑ **corrosion** is a chemical reaction which involves the surface of a metal changing from an element to a compound

❑ corrosion can only apply to metal materials

❑ the reaction involves the metal changing from atoms to ions; this is an example of oxidation,

e.g. $Fe(s) \rightarrow Fe^{2+}(aq) + 2e^-$

❑ different metals corrode at different rates; in general, the more reactive the metal, the faster the process

Rusting

- ❑ **rusting** is the special name used for the corrosion of iron

- ❑ both water and oxygen from the air are required

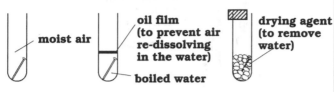

rusting   **no rusting**   **no rusting**

- ❑ when iron rusts, initially the iron atoms lose two electrons to form iron(II) ions, $Fe^{2+}(aq)$; this is oxidation

    $$Fe(s) \rightarrow Fe^{2+}(aq) + 2e^-$$

- ❑ **ferroxyl indicator**, which turns blue in the presence of $Fe^{2+}(aq)$ ions, can be used to show the extent of the rusting process

- ❑ iron(II) ions (black, early rust) can be further oxidised to give iron(III) ions (brown, main rust)

    $$Fe^{2+}(aq) \rightarrow Fe^{3+}(aq) + e^-$$

- ❑ electrons lost by the iron during rusting are accepted by the water and oxygen to form hydroxide ions

    $$2H_2O(l) + O_2(g) + 4e^- \rightarrow 4OH^-(aq)$$

- ❑ ferroxyl indicator, which turns pink in the presence of $OH^-(aq)$ ions, can also be used to show the extent of the reduction

- ❑ the effect of salt and acid rain on the rate of rusting can be shown

iron nail

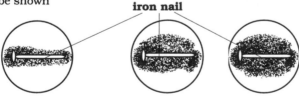

gel with ferroxyl indicator   **gel with ferroxyl indicator and salt**   **gel with ferroxyl indicator and acid**

- • **increased intensity of blue colour**
- • **more $Fe^{2+}(aq)$ ions**
- • **faster rusting**

- salt, spread on roads in winter, increases the rate of corrosion of car bodywork; the salt acts as an electrolyte

- acid rain increases the rate of corrosion; the metal is able to react with hydrogen ions, $H^+_{(aq)}$ which can accept electrons

$$M_{(s)} \rightarrow M^{n+}_{(aq)} + ne^-$$

$$2H^+_{(aq)} + 2e^- \rightarrow H_{2(g)}$$

Iron in contact with another metal

- electrons flowing to the iron prevent rusting

- with metals higher in the electrochemical series, electrons flow to the iron; with metals lower in the electrochemical series, electrons flow from the iron

iron nail

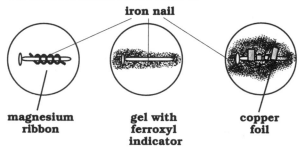

| magnesium ribbon | gel with ferroxyl indicator | copper foil |

- **no blue colour**
- **no rusting**

- **increased intensity of blue colour**
- **more $Fe^{2+}_{(aq)}$ ions**
- **faster rusting**

How to prevent rusting

(a) Physical barrier

- this keeps air and water out,
  e.g. paint, grease, plastic coat, tar coat, plated metal coat

- since no air or water are in contact with the iron no rusting occurs

(b) Electrical protection

- iron is connected to the negative terminal of a battery
- electrons flow to the iron so it does not corrode

(c) Sacrificial protection

- a metal more reactive than iron is plated on or attached
- electrons flow from the more reactive metal to the iron; the more reactive metal corrodes and the iron is protected

Special examples

(a) Galvanising

- ❑ iron is coated with zinc
- ❑ zinc acts as physical barrier
- ❑ if scratched, zinc provides sacrificial protection
- ❑ electrons flow from the more reactive zinc to the iron
- ❑ the zinc corrodes and the iron is protected
- ❑ used to protect some car bodies

(b) Tin-plating

- ❑ tin acts as physical barrier
- ❑ electrons flow from the more reactive iron to the tin
- ❑ if the tin layer is broken the rate of rusting is faster than that of iron on its own
- ❑ used to protect food-stuff cans (tin cans)

(c) Electroplating

- ❑ electricity is used to coat iron (or steel) with another metal
- ❑ this coating acts as a physical barrier
- ❑ used in the chromium plating of bicycle parts

(d) Using scrap magnesium

- ❑ scrap magnesium is attached to iron
- ❑ this acts as a sacrificial protector
- ❑ electrons flow from the more reactive magnesium to the iron
- ❑ the magnesium corrodes and the iron is protected
- ❑ used to protect underground pipes

Cells

(a) Iron/carbon cell

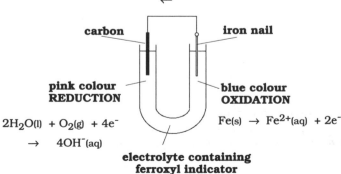

direction of electron flow

←

carbon   iron nail

pink colour   blue colour
REDUCTION   **OXIDATION**

$2H_2O(l) + O_2(g) + 4e^-$ $Fe(s) \rightarrow Fe^{2+}(aq) + 2e^-$

$\rightarrow \quad 4OH^-(aq)$

**electrolyte containing
ferroxyl indicator**

- elecrons flow through the meter from the iron nail to the carbon rod

- the blue colour at the iron nail indicates the presence of Fe^{2+}(aq) ions; these ions are formed by the oxidation of iron atoms

  $$Fe(s) \rightarrow Fe^{2+}(aq) + 2e^-$$

- the pink colour at the carbon rod indicates the presence of OH^-(aq) ions; these ions are formed by the reduction of water and oxygen molecules

  $$2H_2O(l) + O_2(g) + 4e^- \rightarrow 4OH^-(aq)$$

(b) Iron/copper cell

direction of electron flow

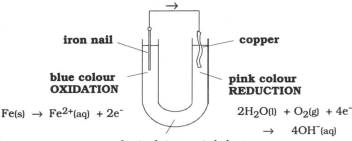

iron nail — copper

blue colour
OXIDATION

pink colour
REDUCTION

$Fe(s) \rightarrow Fe^{2+}(aq) + 2e^-$

$2H_2O(l) + O_2(g) + 4e^-$
$\rightarrow 4OH^-(aq)$

electrolyte containing
ferroxyl indicator

- electrons flow through the meter from the more reactive metal to the less reactive metal, i.e. from iron to copper

(c) Magnesium/iron cell

direction of electron flow

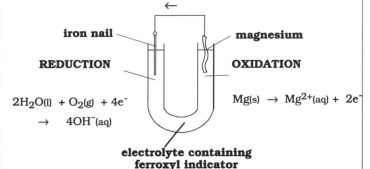

iron nail — magnesium

REDUCTION

OXIDATION

$2H_2O(l) + O_2(g) + 4e^-$
$\rightarrow 4OH^-(aq)$

$Mg(s) \rightarrow Mg^{2+}(aq) + 2e^-$

electrolyte containing
ferroxyl indicator

- electrons flow through the meter from the more reactive metal to the less reactive metal, i.e. from magnesium to iron

UNIT 1   PPA 1   The Effect of Concentration Changes on Reaction Rate

You should know:

❑ how to carry out an experiment to investigate the effect of concentration changes on reaction rate

❑ that reactions which are suitable will have a visible means of measuring the progress of the reaction, e.g. a colour change at the end of the reaction or when the reaction has gone a 'fixed distance'

❑ that concentration of one reactant is the only variable which is changed; all other variables are kept constant

Example

The reaction between sodium persulphate solution and potassium iodide solution can be used to investigate the effect of concentration changes on reaction rate.

Starch indicator (and sodium thosulphate) are included in the reaction mixture to provide a convenient way to measure the time for the reaction to go 'a fixed distance'; a blue/black colour appears as iodine reacts with the starch.

The concentration of sodium persulphate solution is changed by diluting with water; the total volume of solution is however kept constant.

The concentrations and volumes of potassium iodide solution and starch indicator remain the same as does the temperature of the reactions.

For the different concentrations of sodium persulphate solution, the time taken for the starch indicator to turn blue/black is noted and the rate is calculated; the shorter the time taken, the faster the rate of the reaction.

Safety note:
Sodium persulpahte can irritate the skin - gloves should be worn.

You should know:

❏   how to carry out an experiment to investigate the effect of
    temperature changes on reaction rate

❏   that reactions which are suitable will have a visible
    means of measuring the progress of the reaction, e.g. a
    colour change at the end of the reaction or when the
    reaction has gone a 'fixed' distance

❏   that temperature is the only variable which is changed;
    all other variables are kept constant

Example

The reaction between sodium thiosulphate solution and dilute
hydrochloric acid can be used to investigate the effect of
temperature changes on the rate of a reaction.

Sulphur, which is insoluble, is produced.

The time taken for the sulphur to make an **X**-mark on paper
"disappear" provides a convenient way to measure the time for
the reaction to go 'a fixed distance'.

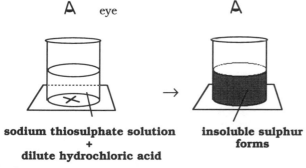

**sodium thiosulphate solution   insoluble sulphur
          +   forms**
dilute hydrochloric acid

In this experiment the temperature is changed by heating the
solutions.

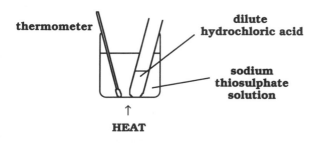

The volume and concentration of the sodium thiosulphate solution and the volume and concentration of the dilute hydrochloric acid are kept constant.

The temperature is recorded before mixing the solutions in the beaker on the paper with the **X**-mark.

For each temperature, the time for the cross to "disappear" is noted and the rate calculated; the shorter the time taken, the faster the rate of the reaction

Safety note:
Hydrochloric acid is corrosive – splashes on the skin should be immediately washed off.

UNIT 1   PPA 3   Electrolysis

You should know :

❏   how to electrolyse copper chloride solution

❏   how to identify the products at the positive and negative
     electrodes

Set up the electrolytic cell shown.

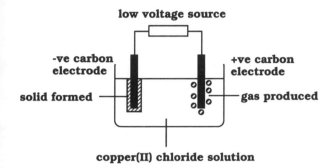

copper(II) chloride solution

A battery or power pack can be used as the low voltage source
of electricity.

A direct current (dc) supply must be used so that the products
form at each electrode.

The electrolysis results in the breaking up of the copper(II)
chloride solution to form the elements.

Bubbles of gas are observed at the positive electrode; this is
chlorine.

The chlorine can be identified by the bleaching of blue litmus
paper or by the characteristic smell of the gas (swimming baths).

A brown solid appears on the negative electrode; this is copper
metal.

Safety note:
Chlorine is poisonous - take a sniff of the gas with great care.

You should know how to test for an unsaturated hydrocarbon.

Saturated hydrocarbons contain only single carbon to carbon covalent bonds; hydrocarbons which contain at least one carbon to carbon double bond are said to be unsaturated.

Bromine solution can be used to identify an unsaturated hydrocarbon.

When bromine solution is shaken with an unsaturated hydrocarbon, the orange/red colour rapidly turns colourless (**not** clear); the orange/red colour remains when a saturated hydrocarbon and bromine solution are mixed.

A hydrocarbon with molecular formula C_6H_{14} which does **not** decolourise bromine solution is a saturated hydrocarbon,

    e.g. hexane $CH_3\text{-}CH_2\text{-}CH_2\text{-}CH_2\text{-}CH_2\text{-}CH_3$

A hydrocarbon with molecular formula C_6H_{12} which does **not** decolourise bromine solution is a saturated hydrocarbon,

    e.g. cyclohexane

$$
\begin{array}{ccc}
 & CH_2 & \\
 \diagup & & \diagdown \\
CH_2 & & CH_2 \\
| & & | \\
CH_2 & & CH_2 \\
 \diagdown & & \diagup \\
 & CH_2 &
\end{array}
$$

A hydrocarbon with molecular formula C_6H_{12} which decolourises bromine solution is an unsaturated hydrocarbon,

    e.g. hexene $CH_2\text{=}CH\text{-}CH_2\text{-}CH_2\text{-}CH_2\text{-}CH_2$

A hydrocarbon with molecular formula C_6H_{10} which decolourises bromine solution is an unsaturated hydrocarbon,

    e.g. cyclohexene

$$
\begin{array}{ccc}
 & CH_2 & \\
 \diagup & & \diagdown \\
CH & & CH_2 \\
\| & & | \\
CH & & CH_2 \\
 \diagdown & & \diagup \\
 & CH_2 &
\end{array}
$$

Safety notes:
Bromine solution is toxic - wash off splashes on the skin with sodium thiosulphate solution;
hydrocarbons are irritating to the skin - wash off splashes immediately;
hydrocarbons are highly flammable - keep away from flames.

UNIT 2   PPA 2   Cracking

You should know:

❑   how to crack liquid paraffin

❑   how to show that some of the products of cracking are
    unsaturated

❑   how to prevent 'suck-back'

Set up the apparatus shown.

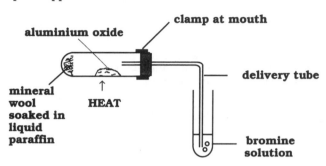

Aluminium oxide acts as a catalyst.

The bromine solution turns from an orange/red colour to
colourless (**not** clear) indicating that some of the products of
cracking are unsaturated.

'Suck-back' occurs when the bromine solution moves up the
delivery tube and in extreme cases can enter the hot test tube.

To prevent the possibility of 'suck-back', **before** heating is
stopped, the clamp stand should be lifted so that the delivery
tube is removed from the bromine solution.

Safety notes:
Bromine solution is toxic - wash off splashes on the skin with
sodium thiosulphate solution;
mineral wool can irritate the skin - tongs should be used when
handling the mineral wool.

You should know how:

❑   how to hydrolyse starch in the presence of either an
enzyme or an acid

❑   how to show that the enzyme or acid catalyses the
hydrolysis reaction

Starch hydrolysis is a very slow reaction but it can be speeded
up.

The control enables the difference in the speed of reaction when
the enzyme or acid is used to be shown.

With the test tubes containing enzyme/acid the Benedict's
solution turns from blue to cloudy orange/red showing that the
hydrolysis of the starch is catalysed by enzyme/acid.

<u>**Enzyme**</u>

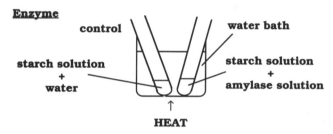

Amylase is a source of enzymes.

The temperature of the water bath should be about 40 °C.

The water bath allows the temperature to be more easily
controlled.

Benedict's solution is added to both test tubes and the water
bath heated until the water boils.

<u>**Acid**</u>

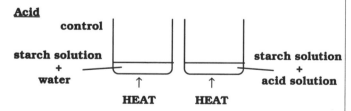

The reaction mixtures are heated until they boil.

The acid solution is neutralised with sodium hydrogencarbonate
before both solutions are tested with Benedict's solution.

Safety note:
Both Benedict's solution and dilute hydrochloric acid irritate the
skin - splashes of these chemicals should be immediately
washed off.

UNIT 3   PPA 1   Preparation of a Salt

You should know how to prepare a pure sample of magnesium sulphate

In the **reaction step**, magnesium sulphate is made by adding magnesium or magnesium carbonate to dilute sulphuric acid.

Using excess solid ensures that all the acid is used up and the salt obtained is pure.

Since a gas is produced in the reaction, the point at which no more bubbles appear is an indication that the acid is all used up.

The excess magnesium or magnesium carbonate remains as a solid in the reaction mixture.

The excess solid can be removed by **filtration.**

The magnesium sulphate solution is collected and a solid sample of the pure salt is obtained by **evaporation** in an evaporating basin.

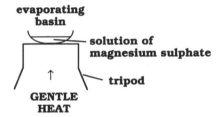

Safety note:
Sulphuric acid is corrosive - splashes on the skin should be immediately washed off.

You should know:

❏   how to investigate a factor which might affect the size of the voltage generated by a simple cell

❏   that only one variable can be changed; all variables, except for the factor being investigated, are kept constant

The size of the voltage could be affected by

*   the metals used
*   the electrolyte used
*   the concentration of the electrolyte

The electrolyte completes the circuit.

For each measurement of voltage, the cell is set up twice to produce duplicate results.

The metals used

The voltages generated by the cells using different pairs of metals are measured as shown.

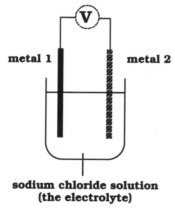

metal 1   **metal 2**

sodium chloride solution
(the electrolyte)

In this experiment the metal pairs are changed.

All other variables are kept constant,
e.g.   the electrolyte used
         the concentration of electrolyte
         the volume of electrolyte
         the depth of immersion of metals
         the distance apart of the metals
         the temperature of the solution, etc.

The electrolyte used

The voltages generated by the cells using different electrolytes are measured as shown.

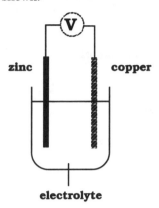

In this experiment the electrolyte is changed.

All other variables are kept constant,
e.g.   the metals used
       the concentration of electrolyte
       the volume of electrolyte
       the depth of immersion of metals
       the distance apart of the metals
       the temperature of the solution, etc.

Safety note:
Hydrochloric acid and sodium hydroxide solution are corrosive - splashes on the skin should be immediately washed off.

You should know how to carry out an experiment to place metals in order of reactivity by observing the ease with which they react with oxygen.

Set up the experiment as shown.

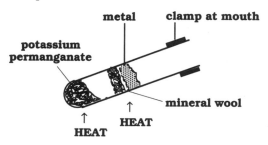

Potassium permanganate is used as a source of oxygen.

The brightness of the flame and the melting of the test tube gives a rough indication of the ease of the reaction.

The metal is heated strongly **before** the potassium permanganate is heated so that the metal is hot before the oxygen is passed over.

Safety note:
Magnesium is highly flammable - apart from when it is being heated in the test tube flames should be kept away; magnesium burns very brightly -do not look directly at the burning magnesium;
mineral wool can irritate the skin - tongs should be used when handling the mineral wool;
the contents of the test tube can come out of the mouth when heating - test tubes should point away from where others are working.